M

se papers from t

NEW FRONTIERS IN CHILD GUIDANCE

NEW FRONTIERS
IN CHILD GUIDANCE

J. H. W. van Ophuijsen Memorial Volume

EDITED BY AARON H. ESMAN, M.D.

*Assistant Clinical Professor of Psychiatry New York University
College of Medicine
Psychiatrist-in-Charge, Children's Service N.Y.U.
—Bellevue Medical Center
Formerly, Staff Psychiatrist Jewish Board of Guardians*

JEWISH BOARD OF GUARDIANS

INTERNATIONAL UNIVERSITIES PRESS, INC.

NEW YORK   NEW YORK

CONTENTS

CONTRIBUTORS

All staff designations of authors and participants in discussion refer to the time of writing rather than to the time of publication. A number of contributors have left the agency or have undergone a change in status during the intervening period.

AUGUSTA ALPERT, PH.D., Associate Director, Child Development Center

BARBARA BANK, Nursery Teacher, Child Development Center

MARJORIE BEHRENS, Research Assistant, Henry Ittleson Center for Child Research

LLOYD T. DELANEY, Supervisor of Group Work, Linden Hill School

YONATA FELDMAN, Borough Supervisor, Madeleine Borg Child Guidance Institute

JOACHIM FLESCHER, M.D., Assistant Clinical Director, Madeleine Borg Child Guidance Institute.

WILLIAM GOLDFARB, PH.D., M.D., Director, Henry Ittleson Center for Child Research

JEROME M. GOLDSMITH, Director, Hawthorne Cedar Knolls School

ALBERT HOTKINS, M.D., Psychiatrist, Linden Hill School

HEDWIG JAHODA, PH.D., Clinical Psychologist, Henry Ittleson Center for Child Research

LEONARD KORNBERG, ED.D., Supervising Teacher, Linden Hill School

LEAH LEVINGER, Acting Chief Psychologist

LEO NAGELBERG, PH.D., Senior Psychologist, Madeleine Borg Child Guidance Institute

PETER B. NEUBAUER, M.D., Director, Child Development Center

LESLIE ROSENTHAL, Consultant in Group Therapy

KURT SALZINGER, PH.D., Research Psychologist, Linden Hill School

MARVIN SCHERER, Resident Supervisor, Linden Hill School

LILLIAN SIBULKIN, Casework Supervisor, Henry Ittleson Center for Child Research

HYMAN SPOTNITZ, M.D., Consultant Psychiatrist, Madeleine Borg Child Guidance Institute

ACKNOWLEDGMENTS

THE PREPARATION of such a volume as this is necessarily the work of many hands. Particular appreciation is extended to Herschel Alt, Executive Director of the Jewish Board of Guardians and Miss Frederika Neumann, Director of Casework Services, for their help in the selection of papers to be included and for their invaluable and continued assistance with the many problems involved in the preparation of these papers for publication. The devoted help of Mrs. Ruth L. Tolins with the secretarial work, as well as with the myriad problems in connection with editing and production, was indispensable. I must also thank the contributors for their cooperation, their interest and, most of all, their patience in accepting the inevitable delays in the publication of their valuable material. Finally, the kindness of the *American Journal of Orthopsychiatry* in permitting the reprinting of two papers previously published in the *Journal* is gratefully acknowledged.

A.H.E.

INTRODUCTION

THIS VOLUME WAS conceived, as the title page suggests, as a
memorial tribute to the late Dr. Johan H. W. van Ophuijsen,
the eminent Dutch psychoanalyst who, during the last fifteen
years of his productive life, devised and developed the treatment
philosophy and methods of the Jewish Board of Guardians. In
honoring his memory we have sought to select from among the
many papers and projects prepared in recent years by members
of the agency staff those which would most clearly represent
the standards and aims for which Dr. van O. stood.

Born in Sumatra on November 12, 1882, Dr. van Ophuijsen
was educated in Holland, obtaining his M.D. at Leyden in 1909.
He worked at Bleuler's clinic in Zurich from 1909 to 1913
and, returning to Holland in the latter year, became one of the
pioneers of psychoanalysis in that country. He helped found the
Netherlands Psychoanalytic Society in 1917, and became its
president in 1927. His close personal association with Sigmund
Freud is attested by the latter's references to him in his *History
of the Psychoanalytic Movement.*

In 1935 Dr. van Ophuijsen was invited to the United States
to become a member of the teaching staff of the New York
Psychoanalytic Institute. It was in November of that year that
he became chief psychiatrist of the Jewish Board of Guardians,
an event which proved to be crucial not only for the JBG, but
for the field of child guidance the world over.

Dr. van Ophuijsen was to the JBG more than a consultant
and teacher, although he was certainly both of these. Beyond
his invaluable services in these roles, however, it was he more

than anyone else who helped to set the clinical program of the agency on its present course and kept it there unswervingly. For it was he who established the Child Guidance Institute as a psychoanalytically-oriented guidance clinic, with its practice firmly rooted in a psychiatric-diagnostic foundation. Sensible as he was of the possible contributions of members of varying disciplines, he led in the designing of the agency's clinical team, in which the psychiatric caseworker assumed the function of direct therapeutic contact with the client while the psychiatrist directed and assumed medical responsibility for the over-all management of the case. This has remained the basic structure of the Madeleine Borg Child Guidance Institute and, indeed, of the Jewish Board of Guardians to date.[1]

In this collection we have sought to show how this plan works in practice. Practice—actual casework therapy with children and their parents—is the dominant theme of the papers here included. This is, we feel, as Dr. van Ophuijsen would have wanted it, for he was deeply concerned with the welfare of children in general and JBG's clients in particular, and was ever in search of new and refined methods of serving them.

It is this searching, experimental approach that we think most clearly characterized Dr. van Ophuijsen and is reflected in the daily operations of JBG. Many of the papers in this book describe new and experimental procedures in diagnosis and therapy. In doing so they reflect something of the professional spirit of JBG for which Dr. van Ophuijsen was in large measure responsible. In the process of such experimentation not only are new ideas unearthed and developed, but many old ones are challenged and sometimes overthrown. This is an inevitable consequence of scientific progress, and no apology is needed for any assaults that are made herein on any established dogmas. This too, Dr. van O. would have approved of. Though it is possible that he would not have concurred with all the views pre-

---

[1] For a detailed account of the structure see *Psychotherapy in Child Guidance,* by Gordon Hamilton (New York: Columbia University Press, 1947).

sented here, he would most assuredly have encouraged and supported the work that underlay them.

The Jewish Board of Guardians is a growing agency. Thus, in the past decade four new institutions have been added to the roster of JBG affiliates. These four—the Child Development Center, the Henry Ittleson Center for Child Research, the Linden Hill School and the Stuyvesant Residence Club[2]—together exemplify the widening of the range of service provided by the agency in recent years to cover the entire age and diagnostic spectrum of childhood and adolescence with residential and outpatient care. While the Child Development Center tries to get as close as possible to the process of psychological growth of every child, Ittleson and Linden Hill particularly reflect the agency's growing concern with and interest in the problems of the more seriously disturbed (psychotic, "atypical," "borderline") child. As these centers investigate the problems entailed in treating such children in residential settings, the Madeleine Borg Child Guidance Institute is carrying on a project in the outpatient treatment of these clients, following even here the interest of Dr. van Ophuijsen who, especially in the last years of his career, was particularly absorbed in the study of schizophrenic disorders. This shift is reflected in the group of papers from these residential centers and by the group on special clinical problems from the Child Guidance Institute.

The purpose of this collection, then, is to present, in the spirit of Dr. van Ophuijsen, illustrative examples of the work that the JBG is doing today, in the hope that it will offer to other workers in the rapidly growing field of child guidance some fresh insights and some fruitful stimuli for further work and investigation.

Aaron H. Esman, M.D.

---

[2] A fuller description of these new institutions, together with a detailed account of the recent work of the JBG, will be found in *Forging Tools for Mental Health,* the decennial report by Herschel Alt, Executive Director of the Jewish Board of Guardians.

NEW FRONTIERS IN CHILD GUIDANCE

PART I

THE VAN OPHUIJSEN MEMORIAL AWARD PAPERS

In 1952 the Jewish Board of Guardians established the van Ophuijsen Memorial Award, designed to foster the production by staff members of original papers devoted to child guidance work in any of its manifold aspects. The authors of the first group of papers presented here have been the recipients of this award. Each of the papers represents a significant contribution to child guidance practice. Dr. Flescher, recipient of the van Ophuijsen Memorial Award for 1954, examines some of the basic principles of psychotherapy and offers some startlingly original technical suggestions. Mr. Rosenthal, who received the Award for 1957, considers a little-discussed aspect of clinic practice, the trifid relationship among client (in this case, client-group), worker and supervisor, and casts light into some dark corners. And Miss Levinger, recipient of the Award for 1953, offers a practical guide to the utilization of psychological test data in a variety of clinical situations.

INTERPRETATIONS OF PSYCHOLOGICAL
1 | TEST FINDINGS TO PARENTS
BY A CHILD GUIDANCE CLINIC

Leah Levinger

THE PROBLEM

SINCE ITS EARLIEST days the child guidance movement has utilized the tool of psychological testing as part of the process of understanding the client. Great improvements have occurred in the kinds and varieties of psychological tests used, from the early days of almost exclusive centering on psychometrics and educational tests, to the adoption of the Rorschach, Thematic Apperception, Drawings, and other projective tests, and currently to the beginning use of tests for brain damage. But insufficient attention has been paid to the way the test findings must be translated and interpreted to the client or client's parent, as part of the total treatment process. Saranson (1949), in a comprehensive bibliography of 339 titles, has only three references dealing with aspects of this problem. Although the experienced therapists and psychologists in their work together have evolved many effective ways of giving interpretation, it now is appropriate to make some of these methods more explicit.

It is necessary to limit this study to those aspects of test findings (and hence interpretation) which are relatively the unique province of the psychological test battery. In the Jewish Board of Guardians, as in many child guidance clinics, test findings are also utilized in a much broader way by the therapist as part of the process of imparting all kinds of information to the parent, such as diagnosis, severity of disturbance and so on. This broader use does not differ qualitatively from the use the therapist makes of his own findings, psychiatric thinking and recommendations. It becomes qualitatively different only in those instances where the parent invests the tests with an aura of "science," "objectivity," and authority, and they therefore have a special meaning for and impact upon him.

In this paper we will deal with instances where the findings from the tests were sufficiently clear and reliable that it was felt justified to discuss them with the parent. The problem of the dangers of the unreliable test, of prematurely labeling a child with insufficient evidence, has been amply treated elsewhere. We recognize that the most delicate of test instruments and the most optimal testing situations still leave us a long way from infallibility. Precautions are taken to make our testing as reliable as possible. The very young, hyperactive or withdrawn child may be seen for several successive test sessions; sometimes a retest several months later is needed before we can be certain of the initial findings; or two separate tests, such as the Stanford-Binet and the Wechsler Intelligence Scale for Children, will be utilized to give confirming data. Other standardized psychometric tests used in this study include the Grace Arthur Point Scale and the Wechsler Intelligence Scale for Adolescents and Adults. (Throughout the paper the term Wechsler is used interchangeably for either form.) The three most clinically accepted projective tests, the Rorschach, Thematic Apperception and Figure Drawings, yield additional material on the child's potential level of functioning and some of the disturbances which interfere with full use of his capacity. In investigation of brain damage, the psychometric and projective tests are supplemented by the Bender Gestalt Designs and the Goldstein-Scheerer tests of Abstract and Concrete Thinking, the Weigl and Object Sorting, Goldstein Blocks, and Stick Test. Relevant standard educational or prevocational aptitude tests are also employed. (See Appendix for specific tests for each case.)

Tests furnish therapist and parent with a clearer idea of the child's current and potential functioning, comparing him with thousands of other children, disturbed and undisturbed, on standardized measures. This can help the parent clarify his expectations for the child, now and in the future, in such reality areas as school, camp, future work. If skillfully handled therapeutically, changed expectancies may modify feelings toward and ways of handling the child. Tests are of least use when the single I.Q. score is treated as paramount, and of most use when the therapist helps the parent comprehend the qualitative aspects of the level on which the child functions. Two children may receive the identical I.Q. of 105, but for one it may represent a consistent level of good, average, sensible reasoning and learning skills, while for another child—who is found far more frequently in this agency—the I.Q. of 105 may contain within it a range, or scatter, from very inferior functioning in some areas to quite superior functioning in others, and the potential may also be different. Qualitative features, even more than level, help determine the precise environmental planning.

The test battery, covering a number of areas of functioning, places the special disability or exceptional skill in a sounder context. The nonreader is so often considered inadequate by school, peers and parents, because of the importance of linguistic mastery in our culture. The precise degree of educational retardation seen in the context of the general functioning may ultimately affect parental attitudes. Or, an artistically gifted child may be expected to function with equal gifts in all areas, until in the context of his over-all abilities expectancies are modified. Finally, the very magic aura of the "test" can be consciously used by the therapist as leverage in helping the parent mobilize for such painful tasks as institutionalization or placement of the child, or of lowering goals for ultimate vocation.

One must differentiate between the two aspects of the communication task with test findings:

(1) communication of factual information
(2) communication of information which, for the parent,

is laden and enmeshed with a myriad of conscious and unconscious needs and attitudes.

Each of these aspects is important, and communicating one without the other may be damaging. We are all well aware of the horrible examples of the nontherapeutically oriented person, such as teacher, student psychologist, pediatrician, who irresponsibly tells the parent an exact I.Q. or diagnosis, without appropriate interpretation. We have tended to be less aware of the equal dangers of the other kind of one-sidedness, where a clear-cut discussion of the reality problems of mental deficiency or learning disability are ignored, muted or vitiated, as the therapist focuses on dynamics alone.

A truism, but one needing repetition, is that a therapist can adequately communicate only what he feels and comprehends himself. The therapist needs more than empathy with the parent's tragic experience. He must be free from any unconscious derogatory attitudes toward dullness or defect, free of "I.Q. snobbery" stemming from his own cultural background or inner needs. Equally important, the therapist must be acquainted with the technical aspects of testing, the meaning of different levels of intelligence and of qualitative differences of functioning, and the practical implications.

Communication means knowledge of how to simplify, what to omit, as well as what to tell. In imparting the factual information, one should be able to discuss the core of the problem, and not burden the parent with elaborate and extraneous details. In communicating facts the skilled therapist learns to gauge acutely the parent's intelligence level, and use the kind of vocabulary and concrete illustration a particular parent can best comprehend. This is not to minimize the enormous technical difficulties and, as yet, ambiguous language and concepts with which we deal. While it is generally advisable to discuss level rather than exact I.Q., this needs to be done sharply. A word is merely being substituted for a number if a parent is told her child is of "borderline intelligence" instead of saying

"I.Q. of 73." A Mental Age, discussed either precisely or generally, may prove quite misleading. Cecily at age seven (see Appendix I) has an M.A. of 3-4, and in many ways this means she has the skills, knowledge and needs of a three-year-old; but qualitatively, she is vastly different from a real three-year-old, in her rate of learning, her attention span, and her personality structure, as well as her ultimate future. The M.A. and the I.Q. can best be thought of as ways of highlighting the child's functioning, respectively from the standpoints of ways in which he generally functions at the current time and of where he stands in comparison to the general population. But, whether the precise numbers or the concepts are used, they must be recognized as, at best, highlighting the general, and need amplification by concrete discussion of the specific ways a child functions and will function in the future.

Feelings of the parents need to be further understood. The base line is the fact that they bring their children to an agency for treatment or for some kind of help, and thus recognize that a disturbance is present, although they may neither know the exact nature of it, nor the presence of disturbance in themselves. While this obtains for all agency clients, when we deal with specific problems of test interpretation of real or imagined intellectual limitation, we deal with very basic parental emotions around producing such a child. The parent may have wanted a child as a glorified extension of himself, and instead has disappointment (such a public disappointment too!), when relatives, neighbors, teachers, the whole community, see the child as different, and view him with pity and contempt. Because of community attitudes and demands, the therapist cannot confine his efforts to the immediate treatment situation. He must, by a combination of direct environmental manipulation and of aiding the parents' search for resources, find ways of helping the deviant child fit into society.

Working on reality needs and goals, one still has the task of dealing with the deep and often quite irrational feelings of the parent. Theories of the cause of the child's defect are expressed in the most primitive superstitions, often by quite sophisticated parents: cousins marrying; eating the wrong food; working too hard; attending a funeral during pregnancy; having a collateral relative with convulsions; and so on, as the mother tortures herself with, "Is it my fault the child is like this?" Emphasis may be placed not on prenatal, or "blood" influences, but on failures or neglect in handling the child: was he babied too much; was too much expected of him; was bottle-feeding at fault; was he neglected for a sibling or a sick relative; was he sent too early to nursery school; and so on. The questions of handling the child usually combine the realistic problems and questions of how to bring up a child who does not fit the community's standards with emotionally weighted questions, such as, "How can I care for my poor little baby?" and "How can I bear this burden that was thrust upon me?"

Who in the clinical team should interpret the test findings to the parent? Generally, consistent with the agency policy of therapy, it should be the therapist who has a relationship with the parent. This is one of the most delicate tasks of treatment, not to be encompassed in one or two interviews, but requiring a period of time and relationship with a therapist. It might, however, in the light of the following illustrations, be of worth to examine certain exceptions where a different approach might serve. When parent and child are treated by two therapists, there are instances where the child's therapist might see the parent for one contact to impart the facts, and then have the parent's therapist work on helping him emotionally to assimilate them. When complex medical as well as psychological data need communication, a psychiatrist might be most appropriate, because of his technical knowledge and role of authority. Or, for a Brief Intake Service or protracted diagnostic study rather than treatment, the psychologist might maintain contact with the parent, to avoid the anxiety and strain of the parent having brief contacts with too many people. This question merits further exploration, for the most flexible and effective use of the team.

We will deal with four types of common problems of test interpretation:

A. Intellectual defectiveness, or gross limitation
B. Pseudo defectiveness, where the parent believes an actually normal child is limited or defective
C. Not defective, but functioning considerably below family's expectations
D. Intellectual superiority

A. Intellectual defectiveness. Since this agency does not offer treatment to the defective child, our contacts are usually limited to brief service, referrals, or protracted diagnostic studies. Besides the limitation of time, we are further limited in our ability to serve the defective child by lack of knowledge and by the inadequacy of treatment resources.

One clear treatment goal is to arrest the almost universal tendency which the parents of these children have to seek repeated consultations, or "shopping." Cecily, Saul and Harvey (see Appendix, Cases I, II, III,), although coming from highly dissimilar families, with quite different behavioral problems, had all been subjected to countless examinations by physicians, neurologists, psychiatrists, psychologists, hearing specialists, etc., in hospitals, clinics, Bureau of Child Guidance, New York City Youth Board, and private sources. Pearl S. Buck, in *The Child Who Never Grew,* has poignantly described this long travail of dragging the weary child from office to office, authority to authority. Mrs. Buck clearly differentiates the two sources of this prolonged "shopping": the need of a mother to cling to hope, and the lack of firmness and definiteness in what the authorities told her. Although Mrs. Buck's account is of twenty years ago, it is striking, among the clients we see currently, to find how little different their experiences have been. Diagnostic tools have markedly improved, but skills in convincing the parents still lag. To help the parents face the tragedy is to relieve them of marked anxiety.

The parents of defective children are a very heterogeneous group. They may range intellectually from a dullness not too different from the child's to intellectual superiority; from a marginal social-economic level to a very high one. Thus, the factual interpretation must be different for each family, with their varying capacities to grasp technical language and difficult concepts. Also, their expectancies are very different. Cecily Smith's parents are distressed that the public school will not accept her, but their ultimate plans are for her to complete eighth grade or so. Saul Drake's mother commented that when his older brothers were four years old, they already knew a number of Hebrew prayers; the first concept she had to grasp emotionally was that Saul is unlikely to go to college.

Clinicians are no longer content with a grab-bag of "mental deficiency," or the crude divisions by I.Q. score of idiot, imbecile, etc. Saranson describes the current attempt to differentiate by etiology, by level and quality and range of functioning, and by prognosis, the "garden variety" defective from the brain injured, the autistic, the schizophrenic child, and others. Research requires this sharpened awareness, but in the task of interpretation to parents, the fine distinctions may be a hindrance rather than an aid, unless they affect prognosis. Cecily Smith has an I.Q. of 52. The presence of brain damage cannot be ruled out. But whether or not any cortical lesions are present is an academic problem for Mr. and Mrs. Smith, who have to bring up this hyperactive child. It is of help to them if the therapist can really convince them, in language they can grasp, and with a relationship that makes it possible for them to assimilate the information, the basic facts: that Cecily at seven is in many ways more like a three-year-old; she will continue to grow more slowly than others; she will fit best in ungraded classes; at adolescence there will be a tapering off of her growth. Why burden the parents with more? Difficult as it is to establish such a diagnosis in so young a child, the observations on and history of Saul Drake suggest a childhood autistic schizophrenia. Mrs. Drake is psychiatrically sophisticated enough to understand this. But interpretation helps her more in underlining what Saul's I.Q. of approximately 40 means. She already inwardly knows, but cannot yet accept that at four Saul is unable to do things for himself or understand others as well as most two-year-olds, and that it is on a pre-two-year-old level she must learn to deal with him.

For Cecily and Saul, as with many defectives, simple behavioral descriptions are often more useful in helping the parent plan than delicate diagnosis. Cecily is limited, hyperactive, volatile, so she enrages adults with her noise and destructiveness, and is also in need of controls so she will not damage herself. Saul is the "good child" or hypoactive, almost inert defective, sitting mutely with repetitive harmless activities. But he is very liable to panic and needs a different variety of protection.

Harder for the clinician to understand, and then to interpret to the parent, is the child with extremely variable functioning (Harvey Rose, Appendix, III). Saul and Cecily, in their test performances and in their daily functioning, are relatively consistent, with little range, and can be treated as nursery school children. The picture Harvey presents is far more complicated, with the roles that visual and emotional disturbances play. Harvey's Wechsler shows average verbal skills, highly defective visual, motor, perceptive skills, and this is paralleled by his behavior. At nine he cannot, although he tries, tie his own shoes, place a coin in a slot, cut his own food; but he can read English and Hebrew fluently, budget his money and travel unescorted around the city. Inevitably such an extremely variable child presents special problems for his parents, with all of the anxieties that stem from living with ambiguity. His mother states, "It would be easier for all of us if he were simply defective; he'd be easier for us to understand, and he'd be happier too, if he didn't have to always try things too hard for him and know he is different." The therapeutic task is to help Harvey's parents see that his efforts and very frustrations represent his drive toward health.

We have best served these families when we were most honest, and we have done families a disservice when we failed squarely to face the defect. Many elements go into the therapist's and psychologist's occasional failures to recognize intellectual defect, and instead carry such children for a period in treatment, perpetuating unrealistic hopes. The following verbatim dictation from the two disciplines on Cecily Smith illuminates this:

First interview: Cecily . . . immediately began to open boxes . . . would bang the nails into wood, look away from her banging and on occasion bang her finger . . . She volunteered no information at all . . . Her response to the doll was, "What is it?" I asked did she mean is this a boy or girl, and she said yes, that it is a "boy-girl." However, when I invited her to look at the doll, she said of course it was a boy, although it should be noted that all these dolls are devoid of penis . . . without any preceding fantasy or verbal production she began to slam the doll on the floor, pull at its legs, and then in a very primitive fashion bit into its head . . .

An interview the following month: Cecily's behavior continued to be very disorganized, scattered, with a great deal aimed at biting and pulling the doll apart . . . on my part explained again how we do not throw out the baby, no matter how naughty the baby may think she is, but we try to help her get rid of that naughty feeling . . . an oblivious attitude toward obstacles in her way.

Following are excerpts from the psychological given in the same year:

. . . she wanted to see everything at once, her attention moving quickly from one object to another. The need to control was manifest by grabbing of materials . . . The reality situation becomes secondary to her own needs and impulses . . . tends to give the impression that she is functioning on a feeble-minded level . . . the results are not a valid representation of her total abilities. Her lack of concern is significant. Hyperactivity and extreme negativism appear to be her way of coping with panic-like reactions . . . Her aliveness and curiosity, coupled with flashes of clear organized thinking seem to indicate that the I.Q. of 50 is not a valid expression of her actual thinking . . .

The second therapist and second psychologist made many similar observations, but came to different conclusions. Also, as in spite of her enjoyment of the agency Cecily changed so little, different methods were attempted to reach her. The second therapist used language and interpretation far less, very deliberately treated Cecily as a three-year-old, giving her physical contact and a few definite limitations. The second psychologist also treated Cecily as a very small child, fed her sugar during the test, but when Cecily's attention wandered, would hold her head and direct her glance toward the materials. With this control it was possible to say, item by item, what was success and what failure and what refusal. As with most defective children, cooperation was good on the items she was capable of doing. Negativism grew as harder items were offered. Having found that she could function on the two-and-a-half to three-and-a-half level, parallel test forms were utilized, until the picture was certain. The test score was within two points of the previous one.

The therapist was able to use these results with the mother because she had solved for herself the problem of emotionally accepting defectives, had a good relationship with Mrs. Smith, and could genuinely point out Cecily's assets of charm and warmth, while facing the defect. The therapist also enlisted the aid of the grandmother and the private school. Yet there was even at this point some balking at the final step of interpretation. In a treatment conference the therapist worked out how she would tell Mrs. Smith, "Cecily is growing much more slowly than other children," and another member of the clinical team would add, "and will never grow as far as others, will never outgrow her defect, will always need special care."

While it is a vital part of the interpretation to stress the child's assets and worth-while, lovable, human qualities, one must not overinflate these abilities. Like many parents of defective children, Mrs. Drake clung to the fact that though he barely talked, Saul sang a great deal, and felt enough musical talent must be present to compensate for the other lacks. But if Saul continues to function as a withdrawn imbecile, it is un-realistic to expect he will ever learn to read music or to play an instrument, unless forced by the most repetitive training. Belief in a special ability is sustained by these parents, but the therapist can help them minimize these fantasies. Then they are freer to respond to the realistic positives which exist in every child.

Finally, there is the question of prediction. As stated earlier, we use tests with great caution; retest when necessary to make predictions safer. Some therapists appear to have an overinvest-ment in treating these children and use frequent psychometric retests, with the hope that evidence will come of raised I.Q.'s. To look at ultimate goals and limitations is important. Studies have shown how in therapy the I.Q.'s of certain defective chil-dren can be raised fifteen or twenty points over several years. Although these studies are of questionable validity, if we take them for the moment as valid, let us apply the results to our cases. If Saul is raised twenty points, his I.Q., at best is 60—still defective. Cecily would be, at best, low 70—or borderline—and, with her labile personality, would still be in need of pro-tection. It is the responsibility of all who deal with this problem to make accurate diagnoses and communicate them to the par-ent, so that he is freed from the gadfly of vain hope.

B. Pseudo defectiveness. Children are sometimes referred from intake worker to psychologist for preliminary testing be-cause the mother's description raised grave questions of the child being too limited intellectually for our services. When the findings from the psychological yield a picture of at least low average (Appendix, IV) or better than average intelligence (Appendix, V, VI), two problems emerge:

(a) Why does this mother need to believe the child is so limited?

(b) How can she be helped to recognize the actual level?

These parents seem to have certain common characteristics. Many of them are quite old or physically under par, and feel the child is "too much to cope with," with their own low thresholds for fatigue and their high standards of order, and their rigidity. However, other parents with similar conflicts over dealing with a child's energy level do not have children with this symptom. While broken homes or severe marital difficulties are common in the entire agency case load, the distinguishing feature in the marital stress of these homes is the chronic devaluation of the father by the mother and her relatives, and their identification of the child with the father. During her interview on the Vineland Social Maturity scale, Mrs. Alexander (IV) mentioned how her husband was so unreliable with money, as she described seven-year-old Norman's poor arithmetic; she made many analogies between Norman's so-called retardation in his unwillingness to do things for himself and the father's immaturity. Mrs. Herman (V) initially gave a picture of a very happy marriage, but in treatment came to express much contempt for her husband's lack of economic and professional success. Her centering on the area of Roger's speech—first, that it was too slow, and then, that he stuttered—appears to have some dynamic relationship with her great overconcern in regard to Mr. Herman's foreign accent. The James family (VI) is more complicated, as Gilbert, the oldest one, acts out as an extension of his mother's repressed violence, but is also seen as a genius, while George's symptoms of passivity and enuresis are equated with the father's weakness. For years George was considered mentally limited by both parents, although his recent I.Q. was 140.

These parents usually come from an upper educational and intellectual stratum, although not necessarily an upper economic stratum. This has many implications. They are sufficiently versed in mental hygiene concepts to believe that a child's disturbance is the result of poor parental handling. They may find it much less distressing to think the child's limitation is fortuitous and irreversible, rather than a reflection on their upbringing. A common phrase they use is, "We gave him every advantage and opportunity . . ."

Tending to have highly intellectualized interests themselves, they have little in common with the normal playfulness or interests of the small child, nor do they seem to have much idea of the limitations of comprehension of a three- or four- or five-year-old. When Roger Herman was just four, his mother expressed concern that he would stand in front of the cuckoo clock, to watch the bird come out, but refused to follow her in counting the sounds. Mrs. Alexander, listing Norman's sloppiness in so many areas as evidence of his mental limitation, mentioned that although he is seven years old, the spelling in his letters is so atrocious, she is too embarrassed to let him mail them. As Gilbert and George James, successively, became engaged in treatment, each of them expressed enjoyment in aimless rolling of clay and messing with paint, because "at home we are supposed to make worth-while things in art and not waste the materials." These families appear to put extreme demands on the child, and then consider him hopelessly limited if he fails to meet them.

Home acceleration is also extended quite early to the community. Mrs. Herman described Roger as the only child in his nursery group who did not talk, failing to see that as he was by several months the youngest there, in this selected nursery school where the average I.Q. was 130, he was highly penalized. She had unconsciously selected an environment for him where he was fated to make an inadequate showing.

The overinvestment in the only child occurs in some of these families, although we lack data as to why it takes this form rather than some other. Similarly, in the two-child family of Gilbert and George James, the sadomasochistic relation of the parents explains why the two boys are played against each other, as extended weapons in the parental battle. We lack understanding of why both parents needed to consider Gilbert the genius and George the dullard, when the two boys both function in a highly superior fashion.

While a different kind of interpretive task is needed for the parents of this group, it is as difficult or even more so than with defectives' parents. The kind of reality distortion they have lived with is hard to shake. They may want tests, but to confirm their belief in the child's limitations, not to prove him average.

Sometimes, as with the James family, awareness of the dynamics caused us to postpone a test until treatment had made the parents ready to accept the findings. After three years of treatment Mrs. James was able to show some interest in George, instead of solely in herself and Gilbert; she had moved so that she viewed George as a troubled and infantile, but not necessarily defective child. Finally, she was ready to request a test, not to prove George's limitations, but as part of planning whether he might profit by going to an accelerated class. Now she was able to accept that he was at least as brilliant as the beloved older boy. Had George been tested earlier, the results, however good the interpretation, might have precipitated undue anxiety, and perhaps even too much hostility toward the therapist for her to continue in treatment.

In contrast to this gradual and planning time of George James's psychological, Roger Herman was initially tested and then retested at the time his mother demanded that the testing be done. Mrs. Herman grew very hostile toward the therapist, who assured her Roger was of at least average ability; played psychologist and therapist against each other as much as she could by manipulative phone calls, and wavered between treatment and taking the child for speech lessons. Even after Roger had been in treatment at the agency for over two years, and more than three years had elapsed since the earlier tests, it turned out to be rather hazardous in the total process of therapy to do a retest. Mrs. Herman's manipulativeness, which had been abating in therapy, suddenly became intensified. The predictions from the preschool tests of better than average potential were sustained, and Roger at seven had a Wechsler I.Q. of 125. The therapist in the interpretive interview did not stress the fact of Roger's superior intellect, but managed to reduce the threat to the mother by emphasizing that neither low intelligence nor stuttering was the crucial problem. Even now it is hard for

Mrs. Herman to accept the combination of Roger having high ability and yet needing treatment. She again suggested her earlier plan of taking him for speech lessons, but finally, when reminded by the therapist of her own problems which she had dwelt on, decided to continue treatment.

C. Below family expectations. Families who find their average, or low-average, or dull children inadequate, in terms of their own needs and goals, tend to come from the same cultural and intellectual stratum as the families of the pseudo defectives. But their concept of the child and their expectations of treatment are vastly different. They tend to underestimate, minimize or ignore the child's limitations, and look to treatment as a means of transforming the child into college material. Often, neither the family nor the therapist are aware for quite a while of the reality problem of the slow learning rate, when so many other symptoms are prominent, as they were with Grace Brown (VII) and Paul Morel (VIII). Much greater sensitivity in history taking and observation is needed to pick up the relatively small intellectual difference of fifteen or twenty points below the norm than of the more clear-cut defective. These children are not sufficiently deviant to be obvious as special problems, except in the context of their over-all disturbance.

Paul Morel, with an I.Q. in the low 80's, statistically belongs to a much more common segment of the population than the group with an I.Q. above 120. Grace Brown, with an I.Q. in the low 90's, belongs to the enormous proportion of 66 per cent of the total population nearest the average. If emotional conflicts did not impede the use of their ability, these two children should function easily in our society, as do the great mass of wage earners, parents, voters. Only in the context of the particular family constellations and particular subculture must Paul and Grace be thought of as deviants who need testing, interpretation of their test findings, and special educational and vocational planning.

The agency's sociology seminar[1] has brought together some highly useful material on the way the culture is mediated through various family pathologies. Prominent in the cultural impact, it has been found, are the marked needs of the urban Jew for intellectual achievement for his children. In another type of culture and community Paul and Grace would not be under the same pressures, but would be thought of as adequate to meet family demands. But in their families, as in many others in our case load, there is the assumption that the child must complete high school, go to college, enter a profession, or at least take a prestige-carrying, white-collar position. Many of our staff come from the same culture, and consciously or unconsciously share the same aspirations. Professional people as well as laymen tend to have blind spots culturally, and assume the only desirable way of life is that of their own subgroup. Living, as people tend to, with most of their social as well as professional contacts narrowed into a subgroup, they tend to lack awareness of the great variety of adult adjustments. Since the children they see outside of office hours are usually the high-I.Q., overstimulated children of their college-bred friends and relations, even they may make erroneous generalizations about child development, and may consider the child who is less than superior to be *ipso facto* limited.

In this Jewish subculture the pressures are generally greater for boys than for girls—again, for time-honored cultural reasons as well as individual family needs. At six Paul was put in the first grade and simultaneously sent to Hebrew school. He was thus expected to learn *two* languages simultaneously. With his mental age of about five, accompanied by developmental lags in coordination and perception, to expect him to master rapidly the symbols of even *one* language was unrealistic. But this was unrecognized by the family and was not picked up by the agency until the second year in treatment. When, as in Grace's case, similar pressures are exerted upon a girl, it seems

[1] For the content of this seminar see Pollak (1952).

to represent a transferring of the usual masculine values to a girl. This was overdetermined for Grace, an only child, with parents divorced, brought up in a matriarchy, with Mrs. Brown vying with her brothers in the field of business.

Test interpretation can be of greatest profit to these families when it is used as part of the total treatment, to help them divest themselves of unrealistically high goals for the child, and see his worth in other terms. In cases where we have been most helpful, we have used tests periodically in treatment (Appendix, VII, VIII). The initial battery was utilized by the therapist to help the parent in the very beginning steps of recognizing the current and ultimate level of the child. Later educational tests were utilized.

These parents do not give up easily. As Paul was doing so poorly in his fourth-grade work, Mrs. Morel energetically decided she would make additional money to finance a tutor. However, when it was demonstrated that Paul was functioning as well as could be expected, in terms of his mental age, she was able, with the therapist's help, to give up the idea of increasing pressures. In fact, at this time she was able to accept the need for reducing demands, and, in spite of the shocked outcry of the orthodox grandparents, allowed Paul to leave Hebrew school. It was of much greater help, in Paul's emotional development, for him to go to camp than to be tutored in reading all summer.

Mrs. Brown wanted a tutor for Grace almost from the first day of treatment. However, she, too, had a good enough relationship with the therapist to enable her to accept the interpretation from the first psychological that Grace was too anxious to learn well at this time. A year and a half later, a retest pointed out the readiness for better application to learning tasks, and the therapist selected the appropriate kind of tutor.

Finally, near the termination of long treatment, retests were employed. For both Mrs. Morel and Mrs. Brown, these were of value in concretely denying their hopes that improved social functioning of the children had meant an equal improvement intellectually. Prevocational tests also were required—for Paul to see that he went to the least demanding type of general high school and did not have to face the trauma of failing in a technical or academic school; for Grace, who was by now eighteen, to help her choose a vocation which met her own desires and aptitudes rather than her mother's.

In addition to the contributions of tests to modifying expectations and demands in the educational and vocational areas, they can be used by the therapist to help the parent change his way of dealing with the child at home. When we consider the qualitative aspects of different levels of intelligence, we find that one of the greatest differences between average and below-average people on one hand and superior people on the other is in tempo of thinking. Paul and Grace, unlike the defective children, can think well, but suffered at home because they could not keep up with the rapid tempo of the rest of the family. When their parents recognized this and ceased giving such rapid-fire orders or explanations, familial tensions were eased.

Another qualitative difference is that only the intellectually superior person can deal with many concepts simultaneously, and quickly apply concepts from one situation to another. Mrs. Morel recognized finally how confusing it was for Paul when she would give him a series of directions, with suggestions of how to modify them. Telling Paul, "After the cleaners and the drug store, stop by the bakery; if there are no onion rolls, get pumpernickel, but not a large pumpernickel, and ask the baker if his wife is feeling better . . ." was just too complicated for him to follow. When, instead, she explained that he had three specific errands to do, he could do them.

Grace was subjected to ridicule from her grandmother and uncles because of her naive literal-mindedness and inability to catch on to their jokes and multilingual puns. Mrs. Brown, who enjoyed the wit in her home, finally came to see how confusing it was for the more slow-thinking Grace. Her recognition that ridicule was so paralyzing for Grace that she could not function even on her own level when jeered at made her change her own handling, and eventually decide to move from the maternal home.

Concomitantly with helping the parents see that these children function at a different tempo, with less range and fewer qualifications in their thinking, with less humor and imagination than bright people, the therapists were able to point out the very positive aspects of their personalities. But this stressing of the positive could only be acceptable emotionally for the parent when a good relationship had been established with the therapist, and when, through our concrete help in school or vocation, changes were already occurring.

Another educational task of the therapist is to disabuse the parent of the popular fallacy that the person slow with language is "good with his hands." Some of these youngsters are far better manually than verbally; others function on the same level in both areas; others are poorer manually. Initially, with her great anxiety and paralysis under pressure, Grace functioned very inadequately in the motor areas. Even at the end of treatment, when many of the emotional causes of her clumsiness were removed, Grace remained far more limited visually-manually than verbally. In contrast, Paul was consistently at the same limited level in both areas.

D. Intellectual superiority. When dealing with parents of a superior child, other kinds of interpretation problems occur. Tommy Lane (Appendix, IX) had, along with all his other emotional conflicts with his mother, special ones because of his 151 I.Q. As too often happens, a professional leak had occurred and someone had told the mother the specific score. Mrs. Lane was punitive toward Tommy for many reasons, but ever since someone had irresponsibly told her Tommy's I.Q., she focused on it, bitterly reiterating, "If he's so smart, he must act this way out of sheer devilment," or "What's the use of all his brains, if he won't use them and behave himself?"

A child at either extreme of the population is singled out by the community in a way that makes an additional problem in the child-parent relationship. He creates a problem through his deviant behavior in a group situation, whether he is fifty points below the average, like Cecily (Appendix, I), or fifty above, like Tommy. Just as the defective child inevitably involves relatives and neighbors in his problem, so the superior child elicits the interest of many people who give the mother his I.Q., promise scholarships "if he settles down" and so on. The therapist, too, must also guard against becoming particularly involved with this kind of child. Some 140 and 150 I.Q.'s are disturbed in a way that leaves them with a cold, sterile type of intelligence, so that only their mathematics teacher is intrigued. Others, like Tommy, have tremendous charm and wit, and with the richness of their interests and imagination appeal strongly to many adults. The disturbed child uses this appeal very often to draw the adult to him and then let him down. We will have to move a long way professionally before we prevent "leaks" in using the numerical I.Q.'s for these children, and also before we can prevent our own overinvestment, which is damaging to the child and parent alike.

Often it is unnecessary or even unwise for the agency to test the superior child, when he was tested earlier. It is often a better therapeutic device to use the previous score, since child and parent know it already, discussing with them why it means so much to them. The parent has to be helped to face the fact that brightness does not rule out severe problems, nor does it mean the child is any more responsible for his problem than a dull child would be. The child, too, will resist treatment for months, scorning the play therapy material as beneath his dignity. Treatment begins for him when the therapist helps him recognize he is unhappy and frightened about "childish" things, which must be dealt with in a "childish" emotional way. Educational or projective tests can be used as valuable supplements to the psychometric, in driving home to the client where the significant problems lie.

The therapist may also have an interpretive task in helping

the parent understand the problem of uneven development, which occurs not only in disturbed children with superior intellects, but to a degree in all superior children. When Tommy came to the agency at eight, he had a M.A. of over twelve, but physically was only an undersized eight-year-old, and in many of his needs was more like four. A boy like Tommy must live with many frustrations as his plans and ideas are invariably so many steps beyond his strength and skills in accomplishment. Certain conflicts and anxieties may be inevitable with this uneven development. An emotionally healthier superior child suffering from similar anxiety and frustration learns to tolerate them. But for Tommy, his superiority becomes an additional source of conflict within himself. Mr. and Mrs. Lane, because of their own pathologies, could not accept this kind of interpretation, but other parents can. Some parents are able to lower their expectations, to forget the glamor of the astronomically high I.Q., as they see what are the child's real problems. They may become less punitive about the child's disturbances. With skillful therapy some even come to recognize that a learning difficulty may continue for a long while, that the child cannot use his capacities in the socially expected ways, and, bright though he is, perhaps should not go to college.

The previously discussed qualitative aspects of tempo, capacity to deal with variables, capacity for wit and seeing incongruity, are present in an extreme form in the superior child. Mrs. Lane could no more follow Tommy's intellectual flights than she could comprehend the meaning of his enuresis, but it is not unlikely that the irritation the former caused in her made her more punitive about the latter. His teachers and other adults, including the therapist, could also be baffled and then angry when such a small child would think circles around them, or unsparingly expose the flaws in their logic. However, the skilled therapist is able to resist this anger, refuse to let the interviews become sophisticated debates, see the intellectualism for the defensive role it plays, and work directly with the child on his problems.

PRECIPITATING ANXIETIES FROM THE TEST

It is difficult to gauge a parent's unexpressed, often unconscious feelings about the test. Even the assumption that it is inevitably threatening is not too tenable. Examples could be cited where neither before nor after the test did the therapist find the parents overly concerned. There are some parents undisturbed by the child's test, either because they are too preoccupied with other problems or are too unsophisticated to invest the test with special meanings. Still, it seems that the safest principle to follow is that a test may contain threats and precipitate conflicts, and one must be ready to deal with the anxieties as soon as they emerge. There is value in having the test scheduled so that the parent can see the therapist on the same or following day, so that before discussion becomes involved in actual test findings, he may be able to discuss his feelings about the test per se.

Mrs. Black (Appendix,) appeared eager to have Sally tested. Afterwards she became distraught when the therapist interpreted the two major findings of the test: (a) Sally was potentially bright, but was not functioning as a genius. (b) Despite her symptoms, Sally was not a schizophrenic child and did not need institutionalization.

Some verbatim quotations from the letters she wrote the therapist reveal, in an attenuated form, many parents' feelings about tests:

. . . Now, what is the purpose of testing people? One, try to find out why they deviate from the normal pattern in order to understand why they act as they do . . . Sally obviously doesn't think in the particular way I do. When we share an experience I come to one conclusion, she to another. I don't understand what conclusion or how she arrived there. Is there any general pattern or general description of her disturbance which would give me a clue to her and therefore my handling of her? . . .

. . . How can I possibly act wisely when I stumble along, not even knowing just what I'm trying to do? . . . My point is that when I flounder, uncertain and unsure and frightened, how can I help Sally?

AREAS OF FURTHER STUDY

This paper has dealt with only one aspect of the much wider problem of how tests within a clinic can most adequately be used. The following additional studies are suggested:

(1) Interpretation of test findings to adolescent clients.
(2) Interpretation of test findings to parents of their own tests.
(3) Timing of tests in the total treatment process, for the child and for other members of the family.
(4) Interpretation of our test findings to related disciplines, such as teachers, family doctors, settlement houses, etc.
(5) A sociological investigation of whether the overvaluation of test findings is peculiar to our urban Jewish clients and therapists, using controls of clinics from different subcultures.

CONCLUSIONS

This preliminary study has dealt with the use of test interpretations in the clinical setting to parents whose children present differing problems.

1. Common to all the families, whatever their own personalities or the child's problems, is great concern about the test, which stimulates many unconscious feelings about themselves, their child, and their role in society.

2. Communication of test findings must contain a balance between factual information, translated to behavioral and predictive terms, and emotionally charged information, which the client needs help in assimilating.

3. For parents of the defective child, it is necessary to be decisive, to help them accept the facts, and arrest their "shopping." Fine diagnostic distinctions are not helpful.

4. The parent of the pseudo-defective child does not want to be told the child has average ability, as he needs to think of the child as inadequate and to place him in damaging accelerated settings. Long-term treatment is needed to effect these interpretations.

5. The dull but nondefective child, who is below parental expectations, may need a series of retests, with specific vocational and educational tests and plans, to help the parent lower his expectations. The cultural factors that affect both parent and therapist must be recognized.

6. The parents of the superior child need interpretation of his unevenness of functioning and some of the special problems that accompany brilliance. Attempts must be made to prevent them from using test findings punitively.

APPENDIX

Following are abstracted case histories of the ten families discussed in this paper. Names and other identifying data have been altered.

I. CECILY SMITH, age 7. Treatment contact January 1951, to present.[1] *Presenting symptoms:* Tantrums, aggression to other children and adults, poor physical coordination, infantile speech, learning difficulties in kindergarten, many fears, accident-prone.

Father, age 34, occupation janitor, limited education, apparently limited intellectually, a fanatical Christian Scientist. *Mother,* age 32, limited education, considered the inadequate member of her well-to-do family, where maternal grandmother and both brothers were teachers. Worked as salesgirl before marriage, till she had "nervous breakdown" at her father's death. Both parents extremely orderly. Maternal grandmother lives in home; is the only one whom Cecily will obey; has protective role with parents; is lame and growing blind.

Prior community contacts: Family pediatrician, private neurologist, private psychiatrist, Mount Sinai Hospital, Bureau of Child Guidance, Youth Board.

Tests: BCG, May 1950; no results given because of her poor cooperation. JBG, 5-4-51, Stanford-Binet (L) I.Q. 48, Figure Drawings,

---

[1] "Present" in all instances refers to summer of 1952.

(unscored) Rorschach; JBG, 5-7-52, Wechsler full I.Q. 51, verbal I.Q. 67, performance I.Q. 42, Seguin Form Board, Figure Drawings M.A. 4-6, Stanford-Binet Vocabulary (under norms), Vineland Social Maturity Scale, Rorschach.

Treatment: First therapist, January 1951-August 1951, second, October 1951 to present. Mother and child seen weekly, father occasionally, home visit to grandmother, school visits. Mrs. Smith brought out, besides the above symptoms, Cecily's preference for wearing boy's clothes, her untidiness and destructiveness, her favorite game of washing cars or windows in a sloppy, repetitive fashion. Mother also expressed difficulty in handling child, as father feels that "nothing is really wrong with her," and as part of his Christian Science belief tries to teach her to ignore pain, allows her razors and scissors to play with. Mrs. Smith from the beginning recognized that Cecily was slower than other children, but hoped she could make at least a slightly better social adjustment than her own, at least finish high school and marry a good provider.

After Cecily's expulsion from public school kindergarten, therapist found a small private school for her, where a scholarship was given. There the teacher provided warmth and limits, and Cecily's behavior and social relations markedly improved. The school was primarily at prekindergarten level, with emphasis on self-help and habit training. Cecily learned to print her own name, but cannot read it, nor any other letters, although in the Vineland interview of 5-7-52 mother reported she likes to "read" newspapers and comic books.

During the first few months in treatment Cecily ran from office to office, was hyperactive and destructive, could not verbalize. Gradually, she calmed down, played in a simple fashion, accepted limits, and developed an affectionate relationship with the therapist, wanting to be physically petted and reassured she was a "good girl."

Mother accepted first test docilely; was eager for retest, as hoped it would mirror the social improvement. Father against both tests, feeling they make people nervous and do not show much. Mother and grandmother responsive to worker's interpretation of second test, and especially grandmother making plans for Cecily's special schooling. While mother still clings to hope Cecily will continue to improve, seems to accept fact she will always need special care. Mother and child both reluctant to terminate contact with agency.

Diagnosis: Mental defect, ego arrest.

II. SAUL DRAKE, age 4. Exploratory diagnostic services, February 1952 to present. *Presenting symptoms:* Development seemed normal or accelerated until age two; then said, "I'm going to be a baby," ceased talking, cried, wanted to be carried, ate with fingers, put things in mouth, sat all day with repetitive play, developed acute fears of airplanes, dogs, etc. *Father,* age 44, Hebrew school principal and writer. Not seen. By mother's description, bright, rigid, passive. *Mother,* age 42, seems older; teacher until marriage; active in various organizations; a housekeeper with high standards; well read in mental hygiene literature. Takes great pride in achievements of the two older boys. *Siblings,* Jack, age 14, described as a fairly good student, fine athlete, initiative in finding part-time jobs, popular with peers; Dick, age 9, extremely good in school, especially gifted in Hebrew and music, plays chess with adults, less popular than Jack socially, tics. Paternal grandmother came into home after grandfather's death, when Saul was aged two. By description appears to have been in a reactive depression and perhaps senile. Was institutionalized prior to our contact.

Prior community contacts: Family pediatrician, private psychiatrist, private psychologist.

Tests: Data on prior tests not given. JBG, 2-11-52, Stanford-Binet (L) (below norms, prorated M.A. 1-8, I.Q. below 40); Drawings (unscorable); Psyche Cattel Infant Tests M.A. 1-9, I.Q. 39; Seguin Form Board (below norms); Vineland Social Maturity Scale, Social Quotient 43. 5-26-52, Stanford-Binet (L) I.Q. approximately 40; Drawings unscorable; Vineland S.Q. 49. No intelligible speech was heard during first test; during second, while Saul did not reply to any of the test items verbally he chattered to himself, and following him from office to office, taking him on a prolonged elevator ride, examiner was able to record several hundred words correctly used.

Contacts: Mother was seen by intake worker initially, and after each test, and by psychologist during the tests. It was necessary to have her in room while attempting to test child, and also psychologist at each contact interviewed her with the Vineland. Worker and psychologist initially had impression of a highly distrustful woman, who anticipated she would be blamed for Saul's condition. She tried to present a picture of a home where the children had "every opportunity and advantage," but stressed that after the paternal grandmother came into the home everything went wrong. In trying to cope with the old woman's demands and eccentricities and the mood changes in the father, Mrs. Drake felt she markedly neglected Saul and was overharsh with him to avoid friction with the grandmother. Struggling to see what her role had been in the child's change and how irreversible the condition was, she shifted in her second contact from guardedness to frankness and marked self-reproach. She related how the grandmother discouraged them from fondling the child, saying, "Save your strength," and

she and her husband had yielded to this pressure. Also, she gradually
was able to relate how she had consistently opposed Saul's regressive
behavior, saying when he ate with his fingers, "That's piggish," and
when he made a request, urging him to be specific about what he
wanted.

In the second interview with worker, she related that Saul had been
an unwanted baby, because of their age and financial problems, and
an abortion had been contemplated. She was ill and practically bed-
ridden a whole year after his birth. The maid, under her direction, had
him bowel-trained by six months; at fifteen months he was walking
well and beginning to talk. There is a marked change in Mrs. Drake's
manner when she speaks of the older boys, and when psychologist made
a general comment about enjoying the nursery school age, Mrs. Drake
replied, embarrassedly, she had never enjoyed any of her children
until they were old enough to "share one's interests." We wonder if she
did not withdraw herself emotionally from Saul, even prior to the
time the grandmother joined the family and created difficulties.

Goals: Mrs. Drake has enough confidence in the agency, because of
our chariness in labeling and frankness in saying we need to know
more, that she is willing to accept the service of periodic retests and
some counseling, and not at this time look elsewhere for help.

Diagnosis: Unclear, functioning on severe mental defective level,
possible childhood schizophrenia, autistic type.

III. HARVEY ROSE, age 9. Exploratory diagnostic service 2-12-52 to
present. *Presenting symptoms:* Isolation from other children, teased or
ignored by them, sloppy at home, cries easily, speech difficulty, eating
problems, question if previous I.Q. of 79 is correct.

Father, age 44, self-educated, well-read, very conscious of his own
intellectual assets, dissatisfied with routine clerical position. *Mother,*
age 42, some college, in advertising before marriage, active in community. Seeing the parents for a joint interview on the Vineland Scale,
psychologist noted their open quarreling, giving of conflicting information, their utter unwillingness to prepare the child for the test
experience, and father's highly critical attitude toward tests. *Sibling,*
Betsy, age 5, a pretty, energetic, poised, very articulate child, whom
parents appear to favor, and report as bright and popular with peers.

Prior community contacts: We have the impression that there have
been many more than reported, with various private physicians, psychiatrists, psychologists, ophthalmologists, speech experts, and so on.
This is deduced from indirect statements of parents of how wretchedly
they have been treated and how poorly Harvey has been understood
elsewhere, and Mrs. Rose's insistence she wants treatment at this agency

and nowhere else. A contact is known at Neurological Institute in 1949, where a series of psychological, optical and neurological studies were done, and recommendations made for psychotherapy and speech therapy, which family did not carry out.

Tests: Earlier ones suspected, not known. Neurological, 1949, Stanford-Binet I.Q. 79; JBG, 4-9-52, Wechsler full I.Q. approximately 70, verbal I.Q. 94, performance I.Q. approximately 45; Bender Designs; Goldstein-Scheerer tests of Abstract Concrete Thinking; Rorschach; House-Tree-Person drawings; Vineland Social Maturity Scale. Harvey showed an abnormal degree of scatter, highly penalized because of his visual, motor and perceptual difficulties; in social understanding often infantile and naive and uncertain; with superior capacity for abstract thinking and good mastery of academic skills for his age.

Contacts: Mother was seen for brief intake screening; both parents and child for the psychological; mother and child are being carried as Brief Service Cases until a fuller diagnostic understanding is gained and an appropriate referral elsewhere can be made. Psychiatrist noted that parents seem to be withholding considerable information. Inconsistencies in the history occur between the two parents' accounts, and in Mrs. Rose's account from one interview to another.

Harvey has had almost no use of his left eye and a limited use of his right eye from birth, the cause unclear. He wears heavy glasses and has the stooped, peering mannerisms of the partially blind. Speech is reported not to have started until age three, sentences not till ages five or six. However, currently he has a good vocabulary, reads both English and Hebrew well. On both large and small motor activities he is reported markedly slow in development and currently retarded, although he attempts to do carpentry, play ball games, and so on. He had difficulty in eating from birth, especially in swallowing; at four was still unable to chew his food, now has food fads and what parents feel are "disgusting" table habits. He is described as very sloppy in appearance, knocking things over, leaving piles of dirty objects around his room; the role of the visual handicap in this is not clear.

What has emerged from Harvey's own account as well as Mr. and Mrs. Rose's is the incongruous division between his efforts to function like a normal child his age and their view of him as totally inadequate. The parents simultaneously shield, overprotect and coddle him, while trying to accelerate him beyond his limitations. Mrs. Rose reports that he was slow in learning to solve puzzles, but she "gave him terrible beatings" until he learned. Because other children shun him, the parents try to share his activities; Mrs. Rose became a Boy Scout Den Mother, hoping that under her aegis the children would be kinder to Harvey; Mr. Rose spends his free time escorting Harvey to museums or reading aloud to him. But Harvey himself says he is able to travel alone around the city, can budget spending money, much prefers silent reading to being read to. He recognizes he has difficulties with his peers, but did not express the "persecution complex" his parents describe. From the parents, especially Mr. Rose, the therapist obtained material on how bitterly disappointed they are in their only son, their embarrassment at what relatives and colleagues must think of them having such an unpresentable, inadequate offspring.

Mrs. Rose, who may have more positive feelings for Harvey than her husband has, after first stressing how "unfair" a measure the 79 I.Q. was, later confided to the therapist she would rather he were defective than have his highly uneven functioning. Straight defectiveness would be easier for the parents to understand, she felt; it would be easier to know what to do with him, and he would be happier, too, if the limitations were clearer. Now he never knows, in a given situation, what he can or cannot do, must try too much and be very frustrated.

To date, our contact with the family has been too brief for us to evaluate the way in which they are utilizing the psychological findings. Obviously, for this complex disturbance, neurological, E.E.G. and ophthalmological studies are also needed.

Diagnosis: Unclear; differential needed between cortical, chiasmic or optical damage; secondary anxiety present, with emotional distortions resembling a schizophrenic child; intellectual functioning in some areas above average, in others highly defective.

IV. NORMAN ALEXANDER, age 7. Brief diagnostic service, February through April 1952. *Presenting symptoms:* Seems defective, slow development reported, currently poor speech and motor coordination, learning difficulties, sloppy and unable to care for self, teased by other children, temper tantrums directed against mother and grandparents.

Father, age 44, not seen. Recently separated from mother, who is loath to discuss him and does so hostilely; profession, architect. *Mother,* age 44, very attractive appearance, but seems tired and older; intelligent; driving; ran her own real estate business before marriage.

Prior community contacts: Details not known. When they lived in Michigan, Mrs. Alexander had taken Norman to several agencies for counseling, psychological testing and hearing tests. While on the agency's waiting list she made beginning contacts with another agency, who felt it was a more appropriate case for JBG.

Tests: Details not known. Mrs. Alexander said bitterly, "They never would tell me anything exact." JBG, 4-11-52, Wechsler full I.Q. 94, verbal I.Q. 97, performance I.Q. 90; Bender Designs; House-Tree-Person Drawings; Rorschach; Vineland Social Maturity Scale S.Q. 108. Norman was very hesitant about trying any task or expressing his feelings, but when he could do so, was thoughtful, realistic, with no indications of gross pathology. Different tests on the battery gave a consistent picture.

Contact: Mrs. Alexander was seen for a fifteen-minute screening intake, where she presented a seemingly logical, internally consistent picture of Norman's defectiveness, and appeared eager for help. She was seen by psychologist for the Vineland Interview; she had suggested she stay in the room during Norman's test, but the youngster was willing to stay alone. Each item on the Vineland was first answered in a very definite way, "He was very late on that," "He took such a long time to do that," but when she was asked the exact time she was able to recall that he raised his head, crawled, held a cup, walked, used his first words at ages which the Vineland rates average.

Mrs. Alexander's own high standards and ignorance about the average expectations for children were evident. She reported that he does write letters, but his spelling is so atrocious she is ashamed to let him mail them. The account she had given the intake worker of his inability to ride a tricycle or wagon were now modified, as she explained he allows the other children to take his toys away but can, when alone, ride them. He can dress himself, but dawdles so she would rather do it. He can feed himself, but is so sloppy that she often feeds him. Particular disgust was apparent as Mrs. Alexander spoke of how late he was in bowel and bladder control, although again the exact times were average. Repeatedly, as she described a habit or failing of Norman's, she identified this as a characteristic of her husband: Norman was so poor in arithmetic, and Mr. Alexander was irresponsible about money; Norman could do so few things independently, and Mr. Alexander expected everyone to cater to him. As she described Norman's fights with the maternal grandparents with whom they were living during these crises, it was evident the grandparents are trying to "restrain" him and help him "overcome" the ways in which he resembles the despised son-in-law.

In the first few minutes when Norman was alone with the psychologist his speech was blurred and his movements jerky and almost spastic. However, as he played with the test items and established a very friendly relationship with the psychologist, speech soon grew clear and movements much firmer.

Goals: Theoretically, this was a case for our treatment skills, to help Mrs. Alexander gain a new image of Norman, and to help Norman become more mature. However, a few days after the test, without phoning or writing, they returned to Michigan.

Diagnosis: Average intelligence, neurotic features.

V. ROGER HERMAN, age 4 at first contact, age 7 now. *Presenting symptoms:* (a) referred for private testing by nursery school consultant 3-20-49, as speech delayed and family fear mental retardation; (b) 10-20-49 retesting, as stammers, fears; (c) applied at agency 10-2-50, with symptoms of stuttering, fears of dogs, dark, injury, shyness with peers, sudden temper outbursts, suspected mental retardation.

Father, age 44, Hungarian-born, equivalent of college education abroad, draftsman, not too successful economically. He is a gentle, diffident man, very devoted to Roger. Both Mrs. Herman and her mother feel he is inferior intellectually and socially to their family. *Mother,* age 35, German-born, education in America, completed college, worked before and during marriage, as an executive secretary. She is a very stylish woman, pleasant-spoken and on first contact, soft, feminine and dependent. Subsequent contacts have revealed great manipulativeness, drive and unreleased hostility. The maternal grandmother lives with them, has a comfortable private income, and helps out financially. Roger has been in care of maids since age four months; entered in nursery school at thirty-one months.

Prior community contacts: The family turned to the nursery school consultant (who was also a member of the JBG staff) and through her, had a JBG psychologist for private testing. Several times they have taken Roger to a speech clinic to have his hearing and vision tested.

Tests: 3-20-49, age 4-2, seen in home, Stanford-Binet (L) M.A. 4-1, I.Q. 94, considered minimum; Goodenough drawings M.A. 4-6; Vineland Social Maturity superior. 10-20-49 seen in home, Stanford-Binet (M) M.A. 4-9, I.Q. 100, Goodenough M.A. 4-9. JBG, 3-20-52, Wechsler full I.Q. 125, verbal I.Q. 125, performance I.Q. 121; Rorschach; House-Tree-Person drawings; Children's Thematic Apperception Test.

Pretreatment contacts: The nursery school consultant and the psychologist worked in close collaboration. Mrs. Herman was dissatisfied with former's interpretation of two early tests, and would phone latter for added information and advice. She was especially dissatisfied with suggestions that time be allowed to help Roger's maturation and phoned psychologist to get names of speech clinics and speech tutors. We attempted to point out to her that this was premature, but the grandmother was pressing for such lessons, offering to finance them. Later in the agency contacts it emerged that the concern about his speech was, at least in part, related to mother's and grandmother's feelings that Mr. Herman's slight foreign accent is such a handicap. The nursery school consultant also attempted to explain to Mrs. Herman that Roger's seeming to be the "slowest child and only nontalker" in his nursery school group had to be seen in the context of his being by several months the youngest, and that this was a highly select group, with the average I.Q. about 125 or 130. However, when it was suggested that in the fall Roger be placed in a younger group, this was not effected.

Treatment. From 10-24-50 until the present mother and child have been treated in the agency by the same worker. Gradually Mrs. Herman has been able to express her high ambitions, disappointment in her husband, and belief that this only child will be the same kind of "failure." She has shown keen intellectual awareness, but little change of feeling. Roger has established a warm dependent relationship, seldom stutters when with the therapist, and through play materials has become able to express his fears and hostile fantasies.

Mrs. Herman wanted another retest almost from the first day of treatment. This was discussed with her in terms of her overestimation of testing and of intellectual successes. Finally, when it was felt that Roger had made gains, a retest was scheduled. Here too, Mrs. Herman's manipulativeness was evident. She wanted to bring Mr. Herman in for vocational testing. She insisted that only the psychologist who had done the previous testing should see Roger. It was felt advisable not to accede to these demands. On the 1952 test Roger was more like an adolescent than a seven-year old, very concerned over failure, and working with great effort and high concentration. After the test he returned to his therapist with far more stuttering and restlessness than usual, and for the first time was able to smash some balloons.

In interpreting the findings to the mother, the therapist did not stress Roger's intellectual superiority, but instead underlined the fact he was free of any intellectual defect. In the first interview on the test findings Mrs. Herman seemed pleased with and genuinely accepting of the results, but returned the following week to raise the question of terminating treatment and sending Roger for speech lessons instead.

Diagnosis: Superior intelligence, beginning psychoneurosis.

VI. THE JAMES FAMILY: GILBERT, age 7 at first contact, GEORGE age 6 at first contact. Gilbert and both parents started treatment in the spring of 1948, George in spring of 1951. *Presenting symptoms: Gilbert:* restless, fears, quarrels with parents, torments sibling, nightmares, vomiting, sporadic eye tics. *George* considered very dull, infantile speech, tics, nightmares, enuresis, soiling.

Father, age 39, a Phi Beta Kappa, laboratory pathologist, former science teacher. He is a boyish-looking man, looking more like Mrs. James's son than husband, flies into tempers easily and quarrels with Gilbert. Had previously had some analytic treatment, broken off for financial reasons, and has come regularly for treatment at the agency. *Mother,* age 43, also a Phi Beta Kappa, finished college at age 20, also a laboratory pathologist. She is a hunchback, looks nearer 60 than 40, is frequently ill. Although she is highly concerned about Gilbert's problems, she has primarily utilized treatment for her own problems.

Prior community contacts: Private pediatricians, private tests.

Tests: Gilbert: privately tested 4-3-47, Stanford-Binet I.Q. 128; 5-11-48, Stanford-Binet 132. *George:* JBG, 3-14-52, Wechsler full I.Q. 140, verbal I.Q. 125, performance I.Q. 149; Rorschach; T.A.T.; House-Tree-Person Drawings; Gates Basic Reading, Grade 4.1. *Mrs. James:* 10-3-38, Rorschach; T.A.T.; Wechsler items (superior).

Treatment. Within this family there is a highly severe sadomasochistic relationship, with Mrs. James taking the dominant, aggressive role. Since both parents work, the boys have been taken care of by maids, seldom keeping a maid more than a few months because of their tormenting behavior. Mrs. James has, since Gilbert's birth, seen him as a child prodigy, with the additional attraction for her of being a very handsome, physically adept child. Mr. James has doubted that Gilbert is such a genius, but has also lent himself to accelerating contacts, giving Gilbert a watch at age five, a camera at seven, etc. Both parents relate that they were disappointed that George was not a girl, and also feel they may have neglected him in his early days, in order to give enough attention to Gilbert, to help him work through his sibling rivalry. However, Mrs. James in early treatment invariably spoke of George as an intellectually inadequate child, while Mr. James has seen him as infantile and the family underdog, but probably of at least average intelligence.

Gilbert never related well in treatment, was periodically thrown back to his initial symptoms, as he was under the impact of the parental battles over him. He has consistently done well in school, and at termination of his treatment in 1951 was beginning to get along much better with other children. With his interests in athletics and photography, he is a leader in the clubs he belongs to.

Mrs. James frequently requested that he be retested, as she was sure the score of 132 was far too low. The therapist took up in treatment her need to have Gilbert a genius and no further testing was felt advisable.

George was eager to come to the agency, as all the others in the family went. While initially he was very shy and fearful he soon began to express his conflicts and fantasies, and has verbalized rather than played. The enuresis and soiling have greatly diminished and his speech is now clear. His school work was, even before treatment, on a high level, but has shown a dramatic spurt this past year. Initially it was felt unwise to test him, as the results would have been misused in the parental conflict. When, during treatment, Mrs. James was able to recognize that George was not a dullard, testing was not needed. The request for it came when both Mr. and Mrs. James felt that George might be capable of attending an accelerated class in a private school.

Diagnosis: Mr. James: Obsessional-compulsive neurosis; *Mrs. James:* Psychoneurosis, anxiety hysteria with obsessional trends; *Gilbert:* Psychoneurosis; *George:* Uncertain; psychoneurosis or borderline disturbance with obsessional defenses.

VII. GRACE BROWN, age at beginning treatment 14. *Presenting symptoms:* Poor school work, "silliness" and giggling in school, no friends, nail biting, untidy, overweight, acne, enuresis.

Father, age 40, divorced, a lawyer. *Mother,* age 38, goodlooking, college graduate, in business with her two brothers. Mother and Grace lived with maternal grandmother and the uncles.

Prior community contacts: None.

Tests: 6-3-47, Wechsler full I.Q. 93, verbal I.Q. 102, performance I.Q. 86; Rorschach; Figure Drawings; Bennett Clerical Aptitude 10th %tile. 2-12-48, Wechsler (form II) full I.Q. 104, verbal I.Q. 105, performance I.Q. 102; Woody McCall Arithmetic grade 6.1; Gates Basic Reading, Grade 7.2; Gates Spelling, Grade 5.3. 6-1-52, Wechsler (form I, abbreviated) full I.Q. 90, verbal I.Q. 96; performance I.Q. 87; Rorschach.

Treatment: Grace and her mother were treated by the same therapist from 2-18-47 through 11-7-51. Mrs. Brown gradually grew far less critical of her daughter, recognized that some of the problems stemmed from the home situation where she, the grandmother and uncles all looked upon Grace as similar to the despised, divorced husband. Also, she accepted that her own quick tempo and sophisticated interests were beyond Grace. In the third year of treatment Mrs. Brown was able to leave the grandmother's home and make a home for herself and Grace. While initially she was determined that Grace had to have an academic high school course and go on to college, she came to see the learning problems as real rather than Grace's negativism, and allowed Grace to go to a commercial high school. However, even at the end of treatment, when Grace was planning on a salesgirl position, Mrs. Brown still needed to urge her to find a position with more prestige.

Grace initially presented herself as an adolescent convinced of her inadequacy and stupidity in every area of living. Her second year in treatment found her able to face going away to camp, and that fall she requested tutoring for her academic difficulties. A tutor from the Volunteer Department worked with Grace through 1949-1950, in close collaboration with the therapist and the psychologist. Afterwards she became Grace's Big Sister. While Grace never did too well in school, she managed to graduate. She has become able to see herself as different from her mother, but still as a worth-while person, and has a few friends of her own age.

Diagnosis: Psychoneurosis, anxiety hysteria.

VIII. PAUL MOREL, age 7 at beginning treatment. *Presenting symptoms:* Stutters, cries easily, teased by children, fear of leaving mother, untidy, food fads, nightmares, daydreams in school.

Father, age 34, fur worker, active in cultural groups, plays in amateur quartet, hard-driven, quick-tempered, self-educated. *Mother,* age 35, teacher before marriage, also active in cultural groups, alert, quick-tempered, a very neat housekeeper. *Sibling,* Nicholas, age 14, was in treatment from 1944-1945, very bright, good athlete, gifted mechanically, planning to join Air Force.

Prior community contacts: None.

Tests: JBG, 3-8-47, Stanford-Binet Vocabulary; Metropolitan Spelling; Figure Drawings. 5-18-52, Wechsler full I.Q. 72, verbal I.Q. 74, performance I.Q. 68; Rorschach; Bender Designs; House-Tree-Person Drawings; Goldstein-Scheerer Tests of Concrete Abstract Thinking; Minnesota Mechanical Assembly Tests, 5th %tile.

Treatment: Paul and his mother were seen by different therapists for three years. In 1950 Paul was transferred to group therapy. Camp, Big Brother and escort services were all given at intervals during treatment.

Mrs. Morel had already, during the older son's treatment, become aware of her own role in her children's difficulties. She had a good relationship with her therapist and hopefully watched for any signs of improvement in Paul.

At first the treatment was so focused on Paul's fears and other emotional problems, that the factor of dull intellect was not considered. After the 1947 test this was discussed at a diagnostic conference. A diagnosis was made of brain injury, probably of post-encephalitic origin, from a severe burn at age two. While it was felt that our goals would be limited, the psychiatrist stressed that we already had helped him become less anxious, and if Mrs. Morel could accept his limitations and reduce her own expectations, further gains could be made.

At first, in interpreting the test and diagnostic findings to the mother, the difficult task was to disabuse her of her expectations that after therapy Paul would ever be as bright as Nicholas, or that he could go to college. Gradually, in dealing with concrete problems, Mrs. Morel came to recognize how the quick-tempoed multi-interests of the family were far too hard for Paul to cope with, and that what had seemed laziness or infantilism was often a disorientation among the many confusing stimuli at home. A crisis in 1948 made this evident. Paul came from school to find the apartment locked and empty, and was in hysterical tears when Nicholas found him and teased him for being such a sissy. Mrs. Morel immediately grasped why this slow child, in need of the known, would go into panic when faced with a new situation. She examined her own handling of Paul, noting where she had been too quick, or burdened him with too many concepts at once. For the first time she recognized how devastating Nicholas' teasing was for Paul, and agreed that she would attempt to ease their relationship by giving Nicholas a room of his own.

The 1948 educational tests were given at Mrs. Morel's request, when she became concerned about Paul's misery at school. It was found that he was working academically consistently with his mental age, and, because of cultural stimulation at home, had a relatively high vocabulary. Seeing that this problem required not tutoring but lessened pressures, Mrs. Morel decided to let him drop his Hebrew school.

A retest was suggested when Paul was thirteen and ready to make a choice of what kind of high school to go to. Mrs. Morel had by now relinquished her goal of college, but still wanted him to be a skilled mechanic or technical worker. Like many laymen, she still clung to the idea that a person inept linguistically might be "good with his hands," although Paul's physical clumsiness was a family byword. After the 1952 test was interpreted to her, she was ready to accept his limitations, and made plans for him to enter the least demanding general high school. Paul himself moved a long way in treatment, in spite of his irreversible brain damage, which was even more evident in adolescence than as a small child. He is now a far less anxious boy than originally and is utilizing his limited ability up to capacity.

Diagnosis: Brain damage, postencephalitis; secondary anxiety.

IX. THOMAS LANE, age 8, contact January 1948 to present. *Presenting symptoms:* Severe behavioral difficulties in school, uneven learning despite superior intellectual abilities, conflicts with peers, daredevil, aggressive, temper outbursts, cruel to sibling, severe enuresis, some diuresis.

Father, age 40, withdrawn, tired, two years' college, interest in philosophy, now an auto mechanic. Has given up most of his intellectual interests, except solitary reading. Shortly after marriage had a breakdown, with depression, inability to work, wandering. Now works sporadically. *Mother,* age 35, high-strung, scattered, though tries to be the "practical one" of the family. Left college to marry. Since Mr. Lane's breakdown, has worked for her father. Feels she has become a drudge. Her large family are successful financially and frequently assist her. Brothers are professional men. *Sibling,* Morris, age five, far more even in his development and compliant than Tommy, no presenting symptoms, favored by Mrs. Lane, ignored by his father.

Prior community contacts: School guidance teacher, private doctors and several hospital clinics in regard to the enuresis. In 1947 went to another agency with plans for placing Tommy, but did not follow through.

Tests: 1947, school Otis (group test), I.Q. 160; JBG, 2-11-50, Wechsler full I.Q. 151, verbal I.Q. 159, performance I.Q. 140; Rorschach; Drawings; Reading grade 10.2; Spelling grade 4.3; Arithmetic grade 5.0.

Treatment: Mother has been seen only sporadically, is unable to sustain treatment contact; when she comes she uses the therapist for audience for her criticism of Mr. Lane and Tommy. Has great anger about Tommy's enuresis, critical that therapist has not "cured" it. Also emphasized the school keeps telling her what a high I.Q. Tommy has. "Then *why* must he act this way? If he really has so much intelligence, my family is willing to send him through college, but not if he goes on wetting and acting like a wild Indian in school all the time." No insight was acquired into Tommy's problems or her own role in them. She was alert for any criticism the worker might make of her handling of the child, covertly accused the therapist of preferring the child to her because of his smartness.

Mrs. Lane has gradually revealed she never wanted this child; in the confusion and difficulties of her husband's breakdown at the same period, Tommy was just more than she could cope with. Besides attempting placement through an agency, she had attempted, just after his brother was born, to send him to her childless sister living elsewhere, but Tommy made such a fuss, screaming and soiling, that the sister sent him home. She not only dislikes Tommy, but is rather afraid of him; she cannot defend herself against his physical attacks; does not know what he'll be doing next; and he is very sarcastic and critical of her in front of strangers.

Mrs. Lane has seemed somewhat more stable recently, as financial stresses have lessened and some of the problems of Mr. Lane, as well as Tommy, are less acute.

Mr. Lane has been seen even less frequently, is elusive and very critical of therapy, engaging therapist in debates as to how the "scientific approach reduces man to something mechanistic and essentially meaningless." He feels there is nothing the matter with Tommy that he won't outgrow, as he, himself, outgrew his enuresis in late adolescence; does not feel the school difficulties matter, "schools only trammel the spirit of a child, teach only worthless rote." Mr. Lane and Tommy have a fluctuating relationship, at times very easy and pleasant, as they play chess or discuss philosophy, at times wrangling until both have screaming spells.

Despite his parents' resistance to treatment, Tommy has come regularly to see his therapist. He, too, has been elusive and intellectual, wishing to engage in philosophical discussions, boast to the therapist of how smart he is, how well he plays chess and reads grown-up books on science. For months he refused to touch the play materials, dubbing them "kid stuff." Gradually, he has accepted the fact he needs help, discussed the enuresis, which has with it pregnancy and dismemberment fantasies, and his many other concerns about physical injuries. Once he was able to use the play material, he dramatized many of his school and social difficulties, and then interpreted the meaning of his play. He explained his use of his brightness, sarcasm and his showing off as a way of making up for his lack of the gigantic physical powers he feels he needs to ward off danger.

Testing was done in the second year of treatment, when Tommy expressed some serious concern about school, at a time when problems there were so severe that he was threatened with expulsion. He took over the situation, giving the psychologist a lecture on the ways emotional disturbance may cause an I.Q. to be unfairly low, how to interpret drawings, and after the Rorschach, inquired if they have ever done a musical one for blind people. With all of this verbalization, he still seemed very tense, grew white with fatigue as he failed the highest items, and tried to bribe or cajole the psychologist into omitting administering the arithmetic and spelling tests, "Now you'll see the Achilles' heel." He was very eager to know the results, and when the therapist wondered why such concern on the numerical score, confessed he feared his I.Q. was slipping, and if he didn't have a high I.Q. he wouldn't have anything. In treatment sessions he then, for the first time, used paints to make his own "inkblots."

Mrs. Lane was mainly interested in the results of the educational tests, raised the question of whether tutoring, punishment, placement, etc., might make him do better school work. She took it for granted that his I.Q. was still extremely high, and found this additional confirmation that his poor school work was his own fault, and used the test findings very punitively with him.

During treatment Tommy has improved considerably in control of his impulses and relation to other children. The enuresis has markedly lessened, ceases when he is at camp. His ability to mobilize and apply himself at school is little changed.

Diagnosis: Borderline, obsessional trends.

X. SALLY BLACK, age 9. Treatment 11-14-50 to present. *Presenting symptoms:* Poor relations with other children, cannot concentrate in school, tells fantastic stories and acts parts as if they were real, bickering with sibling and parents.

Father, age 44, office work, takes extension courses at various colleges, eager to better himself and family, social and cultural standards considerably above his own parents. *Mother,* age 37, some high school, factory work before marriage, but self-educated, with many cultural aspirations, says, "I have the temperament of an artist, but not the talent of an artist." *Sibling,* Mitzi, age 11, deaf since birth, goes to special school, does well there, more conforming than Sally, liked by peers.

Prior community contacts: None for Sally; Mitzi to a huge number of clinics and doctors for the hearing defect.

Tests: 5-17-53, JBG, Wechsler full I.Q. 101, Verbal I.Q. 114, performance I.Q. 87; Rorschach; House-Tree-Person Drawings; Children's Thematic.

Treatment: Mother and child seen by same therapist; father in a few times, feels agency a good idea for Sally, but with his work and studies, cannot come himself. Mrs. Black has had a very dependent relationship with therapist, continually pressing for her advice on what precisely to do when Sally does this or that. It is very hard for her to stick to any topic, but worries about long past events or those far in the future; at time of test she was concerned that in four years Sally would be going to high school, and maybe test now would help her make better choice. Mrs. Black feels her own role in Sally's problems is important, but in her endless discussion of details, of who did and said what and when, she appears to have real problems of separating her concepts of herself and Sally. She is a very literal-minded woman, extremely threatened by any speculative ideas, but at the same time intellectualization is very important for her.

She pressed for the test, with the dual reasons (a) to indicate that Sally was a genius intellectually, even though she has difficulties elsewhere in functioning; (b) to confirm her feeling Sally is so emotionally disturbed, she needs to be institutionalized. At worker's interpretations of the test findings—that Sally was not intellectually a genius but a potentially bright child now functioning ineffectually, and that her emotional disturbances were not as deep as Mrs. Black anticipated—

Mrs. Black grew distraught, asked for more treatment sessions, and began writing therapist daily letters, running to five to ten pages each (see quotes in body of paper).

Sally had initially seemed extremely bizarre as she flitted about the office, insisted upon being addressed as "Your Highness," and conversed freely about the witches and ghouls who visit her nightly. However, in her relation to therapist, she has been able to be more realistic, and no impaired reality contact is noted either by therapist or from test battery. Much as she relies upon her fantasy life for security, she knows it is fantasy. Recently she has become concerned about her lack of friends, and faced that her own behavior may have something to do in angering the other children and teachers.

Diagnosis: Character disorder.

BIBLIOGRAPHY

Buck, Pearl S. (1950), *The Child Who Never Grew*. New York: John Day Company.

Pollak, O. (1952), *Social Science and Psychotherapy for Children*. New York: Russell Sage Foundation.

Saranson, S. B. (1949), *Psychological Problems in Mental Deficiency*. New York: Harper, 1st edition. (In the 2nd edition, 1953, far more attention is given to work with parents and my criticism is no longer valid.)

THE "DUAL METHOD" IN ANALYTIC PSYCHOTHERAPY

Joachim Flescher, M.D.

WE KNOW THAT during analytic treatment feelings are mobilized in the patient which make him experience the analyst as a sort of reincarnation of a very important emotional figure of the past. We call this phenomenon transference. It is understandable that the analyst will play this role in the mind of the patient, irrespective of any psychological or physical resemblance to the person with whom the patient identifies him. It is therefore not surprising that the transference can occur on the basis of the patient's earlier relationship with the father or the mother, or with both alternately and even concurrently. However, there is no doubt that, neutral as the analyst tries to be in order to favor the transference phenomenon, and aided as he is by a whole set of rules aimed at this goal, the inescapable evidence of what the analyst is in reality may facilitate or delay the development of a transference that will be most decisive for the given constellation of the patient. Furthermore, we sometimes discern in a given patient elements which indicate that the onset of the transference would be facilitated if he could be assigned to a therapist of one sex rather than of the other. After having given some thought to this technical problem, I drew the conclusion, probably a too narrow one, that the benefit gained by assigning a patient to an analyst of the sex most acceptable to him is in the long run forfeited for the following reasons:

The initial acceptability of a male therapist rather than of a female therapist, or vice versa, cannot be a reliable basis on which to predict a satisfactory outcome of the treatment.

46

Sooner or later, the conflict around the parent of the "rejected" sex must come to the fore. The question now arises whether when it occurs it would not be advantageous if the treatment were carried on by an analyst of the sex that plays the more decisive role in the patient's conflicts. The issue is further complicated by the fact that an initial preference may be a superficial one, for example on the basis of narcissistic identification, while the more important libidinal object relationship actually involves the "rejected" sex. If we add to this that unresolved positive strivings with an infantile object of one sex entails rivalry, hostility against and fear of the other sex, we must arrive at the conclusion that we shall not expect too much from "sex screening" of the therapist. For the time being, we can use this therapeutic device beneficially with borderline cases, psychotics, and perhaps also with severe character disorders with pronounced doubts about or even open resistance to the beginning of the treatment. We may offer these patients the image of a therapist of the sex which we assume will be most acceptable to them in their current psychological constellation.

Somewhat related to this viewpoint is the problem of the change of therapist. Time and again, both in treating patients who had been analyzed by other colleagues and as consultant psychiatrist on cases who have been exposed to a change of therapist, I have observed the deep repercussions which such an event has on the patient. From the manifold aspects of this issue I shall here mention only those pertinent to our topic. As a rule feelings of great intensity, both of positive and negative nature, which have not been expressed with the first therapist, are ventilated with the second. I would be inclined to attribute many of the successes of the second therapists to this unmerited harvest which they can reap, yet which, to the detriment of the patients, they sometimes neglect to use. It seems as if the physical and temporal distance from the previous therapist gives the patient more liberty to discuss feelings which he was not able to bring out in the original treatment relationship. Such a development occurs more markedly in those cases in which the treatment relationship has reached the stage of a full-blown transference neurosis. This should be surprising, as we have expected from the transference neurosis the maximum which the analytic situation can offer to insure favorable progress of treatment. On closer scrutiny, however, it is not.

In tracing back the developmental disorders of the patient to his earliest conflicts with his moral conscience and with his environment, we inevitably confront the situation in which the infant faces for the first time the problem of frustration aggression directed against the very parent whom the child needs for survival.[1] The magical nature of wish fulfillment threatens the child with self-destruction as the *automatic* consequence of a fantasied aggression against the parent.[2] This in my opinion is the main reason why the resolution of ambivalent relationships with meaningful parental figures is so difficult in the standard analytic setting. It is therefore to be expected that the second therapist may obtain transference material which the previous analyst did not handle and perhaps could not handle if the transference had reached a level beyond the resources of the ego. If this consideration holds true, we have to draw the conclusion that a change of therapist is not necessarily a regrettable occurrence when brought about by external circumstances, nor a sign of irreversible failure when it has been decided upon by the patient himself. It may result in an acceleration of the treatment process and, as such, may even justify its planned occurrence. C. P. Oberndorf (1942) has suggested that if an analyst has not in a certain number of sessions obtained tangible improvement in his patient, he should, in consultation with his colleagues, decide about further treatment. Such a consultation evidently aims at helping the analyst to see what he himself has overlooked in the treatment of his case. With this step, the patient is actually no longer treated by his

---

[1] For the role of aggression as the economic source of anxiety and countercathexis, see Flescher (1955).

[2] As to why this threat comes "automatically" into operation, see Flescher (1951b).

therapist alone. An additional factor comes into being which is certainly not limited to intellectual assistance but has an emotional impact on the further course of the case as well. I hope to elaborate this matter on another occasion, drawing from my experience as a consultant in many hundreds of cases.

Several analysts have already pointed out that intensity of treatment, as aimed at by more frequent contacts with the patient, does not assure progress. Though these analysts are in the minority, they have brought out certain points, the validity of which has still to be disproved on the basis of a more systematic investigation, in order to justify the rigid adherence to the original rules of the orthodox treatment setting.[3] Alexander (1952) speaks about the negative consequences of a full-blown transference neurosis and favors the spacing of treatment sessions and sporadic discontinuations for the purpose of testing the patient's progress and of encouraging his contact with reality on one side and preventing too deep regression on the other. The latter he considers as not necessarily a sign of "deep analysis," but rather as an escape from conflicts on more mature developmental levels. It was he who cautioned that the delving into preoedipal and pregenital material may often be used by the patient as a defense (through regression) against conflicts of oedipal nature. From another side (Oberndorf, 1943; Bychowski, 1950; Flescher, 1953b), the spacing of contacts has been suggested in the treatment of psychotics. I felt that the psychotic's wish for temporal withdrawal or dilution of contact is due less frequently to resistance than to his need to put physical distance between himself and the therapist when his negative transference became too dangerous. This occurrence I found to be inherent in the particular "primary constellation" of the psychotic (Flescher, 1953b).

It is precisely the insight into the transference difficulties of

[3] A thorough investigation could still be helpful in determining which elements from the experience with shortened procedures can be incorporated in our standard treatment techniques. The method proposed here may also one day be found to deserve such an evaluation.

the psychotic which in the last few years stimulated my interest in the question of whether and how much a patient can benefit from a regular opportunity to ventilate his feelings about his therapist. Every analyst knows that such things take place anyway and, not rarely, without the therapist's being told at all or, at best, told only long after they have occurred. The cathartic benefit of such extratherapeutic disclosures is usually offset by the ensuing guilt feelings. Frequently no reference is made to such an occurrence unless the therapist guesses it from the material brought by the patient. In any case, the fact remains that, after the patient has "confessed" to the analyst that he has shared his feelings regarding him with somebody else, a definite amelioration of the treatment atmosphere takes place.

All the above elements concurred in the formulation in my mind of the final question: *Why should psychological treatment be rendered by only one person?* Given the multiplicity of the transference needs (dependency, sexuality, idealization, etc.) which have to be progressively worked through, this rule is not self-explanatory. Furthermore, the conflictual situation which Freud has considered as nuclear to every mental disorder, that is, the oedipal situation, is not centered in the relationship with one parent alone but with both of them. It is self-evident that whatever the genetic history of the patient is, an analysis cannot be regarded as successful if it has not solved problems related to this constellation. In addition, following Alexander's train of thought, one could say that the dilemma of regression to pregenitality as a defense against oedipal conflicts can be translated into the dilemma of fostering dependency needs on a preoedipal parental figure, at the expense of the progress to that developmental phase in which the heterosexual attraction asserts a greater influence than the fulfillment of anaclitic (dependency) needs. This phase, however, involves *both* parents, be it in the normal or in the inverted oedipal situation.

My experience both as an analyst and as consulting psychiatrist in the Madeleine Borg Child Guidance Institute has further taught me that ambivalent attitudes rooted in the relationship of the infant to the mother play a decisive role in structuring the relationship with the parents as a couple (Flescher, 1955). The original ambivalence toward the preoedipal object is often used to increase the inevitable clash with the rival parent in the oedipal situation, thus increasing the fear of the latter to a degree which is neither explainable by the objective attitude of this parent toward the child nor by the possible current overstimulation and increased danger of seduction. The mechanism of "ambivalence clearance," which I have described as a defense (1951a), can here be seen frequently in pure culture. On the other hand, we know that, when the child complains to one parent about the other, it will be largely the parent's method of handling the child's accusations that will decide whether the child will again be reconciled with or will withdraw from the parent who, in reality or fantasy, has hurt him. Every analyst will have accumulated rich evidence of the fact that the typical conflicts of the child in the oedipal situation and around sexual identification gain pathogenic intensity by the nature of the emotional relationship between the parents and the way in which they "interpret" to the child each other's role and status.

If we now epitomize the main elements of our train of thought, that is, the difficulties related to the role of ambivalence in the transference on the analyst, the beneficial effect of para-analytic catharsis of transference feelings, the dilemma about therapeutically intended regression to pregenitality and its defensive alternative, and the triangular nature of the oedipal situation, it appears that we have sufficient theoretical grounds to be encouraged in *providing the patient with the analytical assistance of two therapists of opposite sex with whom he is to have contact alternately.* The setup will thus closely approximate the parental situation. The benefits which we may expect from this expanded treatment are the following:

1. Intensive feelings stemming from positive transference will be more easily expressed with the other therapist in cases where strong inferiority feelings, narcissistic sensitivity or fear

of one's own hostility in the event of rejection interfere with their utterance to the object of these feelings.

2. A positive transference instituted out of a defense against hostile feelings considered by the patient as dangerous will be less likely to be misunderstood by the alternate therapist. Conversely, spontaneous or defensive hostility will be more easily "ventilated from a distance," and will therefore be less apt to produce disturbing countertransference phenomena.

3. The heterosexual attraction, which certainly plays a role also in the treatment relationship, will favor polarization of the libidinal needs of the patient without bringing him into conflict with the results of his reality testing concerning the actual sex of the therapist.

4. The feeling of dealing with two parental figures will give the patient a sort of protection against any anticipatory fear of retaliation on the part of either of them. He will be less threatened by the common fantasy of being completely under the domination of one therapist only who, both in reality and through projection, becomes in analytic therapy an all-powerful figure whom no one checks regarding his arbitrariness.

5. Strong dependency needs will be counteracted by the reproduction, through this type of setting, of the oedipal situation which may thus offer the best antidote against entrenchment of preoedipal and pregenital regression as a defense against oedipal and genital strivings.

6. Identification processes of decisive importance for both ego development and sexual identity will be channeled much more easily in the right direction through the availability, in every case, of a therapist of the same sex as the patient.

7. The way in which the patient will relate to one or another analyst will provide much earlier clues concerning both content and defense connected with the patient's unresolved problems.

8. Integration conferences between the two therapists will help both to distinguish much more precisely between defense and content.

9. Transference phenomena in the standard setup often con-

tinue under a very highly libidinized form but, strangely enough, without any progress in relationships with people outside the treatment situation, because of the unrecognized motive of conspiracy with the therapist of the opposite sex or because of overstrong guilt feelings and fear of the too-threatening therapist of the same sex. The dual setup will counteract this through the patient's realizing that the therapist of his own sex is very well aware of and accepts the expression of his heterosexual strivings.

10. Countertransference phenomena of a positive nature will not reach a degree unfavorable to the progress of therapy. The parental setting of the treatment is more conducive to the analyst's awareness that, whatever the age of the patient, both the conflicts and the participating trends are of infantile nature, and that he, the therapist, contrary to the patient's frequent reiteration at the height of positive transference, is never a contemporary mate but a parental figure.

11. Countertransference responses of every nature, just because they remain unexpressed, often accumulate in intensity to the point of influencing decisively the therapist's approach. The integration conferences where such feelings, be they positive or negative, will come to the fore, may, to a large degree, eliminate this source of technical errors.

I anticipated that objections might be raised that interpretation of the material (behavior patterns, fantasies, dreams, slips, etc.) brought to two different analysts will hardly coincide. This may therefore lead to a confusion of the patient and to a loss of his confidence in both therapists. I reasoned that this situation is not much different from that of the child who can hardly expect that both parents will maintain the same attitude and react in the same way to whatever he has experienced or expressed. The patient will certainly agree or disagree prejudicially with interpretations made by one or the other analyst. The opportunity of expressing one's reaction to a given interpretation to the second analyst will not only be of benefit to the patient through cathartic dilution of its possible aftereffects, but the second therapist will be offered invaluable elements to judge if an acceptance was merely intellectual or due only to transference, if a refusal was due to resistance, if an increase of symptomatic complaints (negative therapeutic reaction) stemmed from the "incompleteness" of interpretation, and so forth. With greatest likelihood, one of the two analysts will become the preferred object of superego or ego-ideal projection; thus the other analyst will have the opportunity to analyze the projection in an experimental setting, and to size up the implied reality distortions. It was my feeling that, whatever diversity in personality and training of the analysts there may be, it will, in the practical operation, reveal itself as a minor drawback in comparison with the positive influence of the new treatment setting.

I foresaw that we may find motives of resistance against this new setting in the therapists as well as in patients, especially in certain types of the latter. Psychotherapy, including analysis, favors unconscious, narcissistic fantasies of omnipotence in the therapist whose daily empathetic effort is to delve into the magical thought processes of the patient (Flescher, 1941). Emotional elements of this and similar natures may discourage a therapist from sharing a case with another on equal terms. The therapist who works alone, even if he is supervised, is likely, consciously or unconsciously, to screen the communicable material down to what he wishes to reveal to his supervisor or control analyst.[4] I anticipated that in the dual setup, each therapist would, through contact with the patient, have the advantage of the most direct source of information.

In reference to patients, it had to be considered that many have no inkling, or sometimes only a vague intellectual notion, of the relationship between their symptoms and instinctual drives. As many of them may feel, at least on a conscious level, that their goals are basically different from those connected

[4] See confirmation of this assumption on page 72.

with their past family life, they might be puzzled by this new type of treatment setting and annoyed by its implications. A specific example comes to my mind of a type of patient whose character Freud regarded as a liability, though I personally am less inclined to consider it so. I refer to the kind of woman who, because of her masculine strivings, comes into treatment with the basic expectation of achieving the masculine status. Such a woman, having often developed pronounced professional or artistic ambitions, and being far removed from issues of womanhood or motherhood, may display a negative attitude toward this method. However, I saw no ground to extend such an eventuality beyond its scope. Even here I considered the possibility of including a second analyst at an appropriate stage of treatment.

The above theoretical considerations were formulated by me during the year 1952. At the beginning of 1953 I submitted them, together with a questionnaire, to four leading authorities in the psychoanalytic field.[5] In the conviction that the analytic treatment was the most causal therapeutic method, I wished to make sure that there were no contraindications to experiment with the presented method, though I was convinced that there were none.

In the questionnaire the following main points were raised: (1) Is there any basic theoretical principle which is violated through the proposed expansion of analytic treatment? (2) Are there elements of practical nature gathered from the past application of the analytic method which would make it appear unfeasible to experiment with the proposed method?

Two recipients, both pioneers of psychoanalysis (one in this country and the other in Great Britain), answered that they did not see that the proposed method was contradictory to any of the basic principles of psychoanalytic treatment. The first also added that there was no element from his past experience with the psychoanalytic method that would speak against my

---

[5] For obvious reasons, I have limited the number of correspondents.

experimentation. As the two other colleagues did not answer this basic question, I must consider their omission in the same sense as the statements of the first two. In general, no one discouraged me from undertaking the experiments. Instead, my correspondents felt, with varying degrees of interest, that I should test my assumption through practical application. One recipient, besides being very encouraging, expressed the opinion that the personality of the therapist was perhaps more important than the method. Another correspondent, however, thought that I underrated the tremendous difficulties, especially as to transference and to reality testing, which the modified analytic situation would of necessity entail. I concluded that the writer might perhaps have in mind the countertransference difficulties rather than the difficulty of the patient to relate to two therapists. An essential characteristic of dual therapy is precisely the possibility of developing a mother- and a father-transference to two different persons instead of superimposing one on the other. Around the countertransference difficulties, I reasoned that they cannot possibly be greater than those met in individual analysis. On the contrary, I feel that irrational responses on the part of the therapist might become evident more quickly in the new setting,[6] not only to the member of the dual team but also to the patient. To give a practical example: an unconscious wish to monopolize the patient, for whatever countertransference reasons, will become much more apparent and therefore also much easier to control in a dual setting than in individual treatment.

My convictions were even firmer about the topic of reality testing. I know that one of the chief tasks of analytic therapy is to improve our patients' reality testing and to make them aware of the distortions to which they may fall victim under the impact of their unconscious needs. Therefore I did not think it obligatory to exploit their handicap, if this can be avoided. Such is the case when there are two objects ready to assume the roles of the two parental figures who played different parts in

[6] This may hold true for all the *defensive, reactive,* and *induced* types of countertransference described by me (1953a).

the changing strivings of the growing child. It was just the avoidance of the usual situation in which the patient's reality testing is overburdened by the need to polarize, on the transference level, a multiplicity of wishes and responses on only one therapist, that I considered one of the major values of the new technique.

As there were initially some difficulties in selecting a dual team, I myself started, in two separate offices of the Madeleine Borg Child Guidance Institute of the Jewish Board of Guardians, to treat a girl (Patient B.R.) and a boy (Patient P.M.) within the frame of this setup. Another team was later on provided by two psychiatric social workers for Patient A.L. Recently I included a female therapist in the treatment of a borderline psychosis (Patient E.F.) who had returned to me a few months previously.[7] Except for a short period in two cases the standard frequency of contacts with the patient was one per week (alternate weeks with each therapist).

CLINICAL ILLUSTRATIONS

Case 1

Patient B.R., a fourteen-and-one-half-year-old girl, diagnosed initially as anxiety hysteria, had extreme temper tantrums, during which she would physically attack her mother. There was strong sibling rivalry with a younger brother. She was sloppy, did not bathe and refused to go to school. She would use vile language, and live on the fringe of delinquent groups. She had recently been physically examined at the police station because she was suspected of being a member of a "non-virgin" club. Three years earlier, she had nightmares connected with a fear that her girl friend's death from polio had been concealed from her. Her mother also started being intensely fearful of the possible contagion with polio. In the mother's history we found extreme rivalry with younger siblings, fears of illness, and death of a sister, and an unusual closeness to the grandmother with whom she had slept in the same bed almost to the time of the latter's death from cancer. The daughter was unsuccessfully treated by a female worker for nine months. She displayed toward her therapist an increasing suspicious-

[7] At the date of this draft the dual method has been applied in twelve cases.

ness and ended up by attacking her physically, insisting that she be given her record. She also tried to force her way into the record room. B. clamored that we were considering her crazy and refused to continue treatment.

Placing the girl in a psychiatric hospital for observation against her will would have duplicated the controlling attitude of her mother who, in reality, watched her every step and curtailed her every activity. We introduced the dual setup, with weekly alternate contacts. Within two interviews, B.'s suspiciousness of the Institute and of the worker abated. She still questioned her need to come for treatment, but she talked more freely, giving such previously withheld information as that she had a Gentile boy friend. In contrast to her former clamorously defiant attitude, she appeared appealing and warm in the interview situation. With her boy friend, she developed a steady relationship which had to be considered normal in every aspect, in so far as she visited his family whom she respected and by whom she was warmly accepted. The boy, being of a different religion, was, however, excluded from her home. B.'s mother adamantly refused to admit him, though she allegedly was "tortured" by the possibility that her daughter might engage in sexual promiscuity elsewhere. All attempts to influence the mother's acting out of her problem with her daughter were fruitless. Notwithstanding this, B. continued to improve except in one area: she did not wish to go to school. The mother, having finished her own studies, was over-involved in her daughter's school life. B. complained that her school achievements, which in the past had been outstanding, were used by her mother only to impress the teachers.

The patient wished to become independent of her parents very soon, and the only way in which she could do it was to find a job. (Her boy friend was a conscientious worker who shared his earnings with his family.) While before she appeared disheveled and gypsy-like, now she was neat and well-groomed. After nineteen alternate interviews, the patient, who had previously refused to continue treatment because her name appeared in our files, insisted on having a psychological test at our Institute in order to evaluate her job assets. While she had in the past insisted that nobody at home, including her father, cared for her, in one of the last interviews (M10),[8] she remarked that the only person who really cared about her and who was warm and affectionate toward her was her father. The relationship with her mother improved after the fifteenth interview, and physical battles with her have com-

[8] F1—first interview with female therapist, M1—first interview with male therapist.

pletely ceased. B.R. has taken a job and lost her interest in continuing treatment.

Excerpts from interview material: In M1, patient is clamorous in her suspiciousness and defiance, speaks about other people needing psychiatric help more than she; she considers the Institute as an extension of the police, brings examples of brutality in law enforcement. Toward the end of the first interview, there appears an unexpected, new meaning in her insistence on not having a record in the Institute: she doesn't wish "to be considered a number, case or record, but a human being." Doesn't believe my interest in her can be genuine, as I am seeing hundreds of other children (sibling rivalry). Mother knows a lot about psychiatry, and, if I would see her, she could sway me to her side (mother a powerful figure against whom father could not stand up).

In interview F1, patient's appearance greatly improved. B. says, "Children don't know the score and get themselves into real scrapes," and "I have had too many experiences." (Increase in reality testing contrary to the past "I wish to do whatever I like" attitude.) In following integration conference, female worker's overconcentration on what went on between the male therapist and the patient became apparent, and was found to play into this child's suspicion of being watched.

In M2, patient admits friendship with boy, shows strong, positive transference with oversensitivity around time limit. Through memory slip, B. comes one week too early to male therapist. In F4, she "guesses that she might need two therapists because 'I am perhaps doubly treacherous.'" Discusses deep aversion to school and again her need for independence. Says she is concealing from boy friend that she is coming to a psychiatric agency. Is sarcastic about tests given by her mother's "psychiatrist friends" when she was a child. A stronger transference toward male therapist is evident, though significantly interview is dedicated mostly to wish to earn money quickly in order to buy expensive clothes. B. refuses to give name of boy friend. (Male therapist was the first to whom she told it.)

In F5, B. talks of continuing visits to boy's family whom she likes very much and who accept her. She is defensive about her reaction to boy's plan to enter army. Female therapist, through a slip, betrays fear of girl's running off to marry boy friend, which in this case was a countertransference reaction. (Shortly afterwards, a violent quarrel broke out over the question of mother's promise of money as inducement for B. to go to school; daughter tried to choke mother.) She says she prefers to work for men; she always gets along better with male teachers. (In last school experience, an extremely disturbed one, she made friends with school dean.) In M5, she complains that parents, siding with her brother, urge her to give in to him because she is grown up. In F6, therapist remarked on striking change in B.'s appearance, connecting it with her coming to see me. B. reacted to this by deciding not to come to see me any more. The tangible repercussion of increase of guilt feelings was handled appropriately, conforming to our insight. The patient continued to see me.

In M6, she complains about father's telling her not to come home if she can't be on time, and about parents' referring to "their" home, which she would never do with her own children. Describes how sad she is and how she wants to cry when parents don't speak to her. In M7, she mentions that father told her she can leave home immediately after she had said she wished she were eighteen so she could be on her own. In M8, she complains about parents' still siding with brother and not caring for her. Speaks about privileges of male sex and of her past tomboyish activities. Still defensive about boy friend; seems to have trouble describing him, but speaks rather about a girl friend who is in the same predicament with her family because of boy friend's different religion. Says that parents are usually unaware of their children's wish to lead independent life. In F9, therapist obtains significant material on child's struggle against dependency needs, and rightly concludes that patient, by attempting to become economically independent, wishes to feed herself as mother did not feed her. In F11, patient reveals to female therapist that she belongs to a girls' club, which fact she conceals from mother. Therapist recognizes that girl continually teases mother by hiding plans of social activities, leaving mother with tormenting belief of daughter's engaging in promiscuity. The patient revealed also how she herself brought about the traumatic examination at the police station. She had been denounced for promiscuity by a sexually delinquent girl whom she had teased by insinuating that she had had intimate contacts with boy friends of this girl. In the same interview, B. remembers how mad she used to get. She would go into the street, bump into somebody, and then yell at this person for bumping into her.

In the subsequent alternate interviews the relationship with the parents appeared definitely improved. B. spoke realistically, especially with the female therapist, about her plan to marry her boy friend after a few years, should their relationship continue to be satisfactory. In the same manner, she discussed job facilities and asked for aptitude test. When both therapists faced her with the fact that in the psychological examination, emotional problems too are explored, she raised no objections. Her attitude toward her brother changed; she now took some responsibilities for him, assuming the mother's role. Reality factors led to some irregularity in our contacts, with repercussion on the client only in the transference: she again complained of our limited and pretended interest in her because we gave her only forty-five minutes and saw many children before and after her interview. The motive for incapacity to share the teacher became apparent. Though the female therapist inadvertently had stressed her superego role in the oedipal situation, the girl's dependency needs evidently supplied the most important source for the positive transference which she developed toward the female therapist, with whom she shared, without resistance, all her thoughts around her future plans.

All attempts to influence the mother's overinvolvement with the daughter were of no avail. Her interference in B.'s life and her overprotectiveness were not only a re-enactment (in a reversed role) of her unfulfilled dependency needs, but were an important defense against her awareness of sexual attachment and hatred against female figures of her past (her mother and grandmother).

Though we knew that the interruption of the patient's school career was irrational, it still appeared to be the best solution in her condition. The possibility for her to be economically independent, to improve her self-image which had been severely impaired also by the birth of a brother, to escape the threat of homosexual regression under the influence of her mother represented the positive aspect of the patient's decision. (See follow-up on this case in note on page 74.)

Case 2

Patient P.M., a thirteen-year-old boy, was referred to the Child Guidance Institute toward the end of 1946 because of his continual crying since infancy, his need to drink great quantities of water, his pollakiuria, his stuttering, and his fears of sharp instruments and of death. The latter developed following his grandmother's death. The diagnosis was anxiety hysteria with compulsive elements. Since I have been supervising the case, the borderline nature of the presented syndrome has become increasingly evident. The mother admitted having wanted a daughter. She has been overprotective and at the same time deprecating toward her son. The father, when the boy was four, would threaten that his penis would fall off if he did not control his frequent urination. Both parents were even currently extremely seductive toward him.

The patient had been treated by a male worker until September 1948. During this period, the striking material that came to the surface revealed a basic ego weakness and severe impairment of reality testing (anxieties of having, through masturbation, impregnated his mother and maternal grandmother). Incestuous and homosexual fantasies became the focal point of his treatment by the second male worker, which continued until November 1950. It was during the second treatment period that I took over the supervision of this case. It soon became evident that the intention of the second worker, to free the youngster from his admitted wish to have his mother for himself "by offering him warm permissiveness and acceptance," went beyond the desired goal. The therapist's approach was an expression of strong countertransference, the nature of which interfered with the boy's progress since it increased his homosexual panic. The countertransference attitude— of defensive type (Flescher, 1953a)—was deeply entrenched in the therapist and not manageable in supervision. I decided to transfer the patient to a female therapist.

Neither parent was amenable to treatment; they both used all their influence to separate the youngster from therapy and at the same time would very often show themselves in the nude to him, thus exacerbating his sexual conflicts regarding them both. We decided to work toward the goal of the patient's leaving home. The greatly gifted boy would write original (as far as I could judge) poems centering on masochism, on homosexuality, and on his "oneness with Christ." He would periodically refuse to eat and drink; subsequently he would take large amounts of food and water, though at the same time expressing aversion to becoming "as fat and distasteful as his father." The patient reported with desperation that his mother, when encouraging him to eat, would say that he "would certainly like to have a double chin." He withdrew from any outside relationship because of his fear of being attacked: "Life outside is full of people who wish to knock others down." The female worker, supervised by me in biweekly conferences, succeeded in eliciting valuable material which permitted us to grasp a few of the basic problems of the boy. Intercourse was perceived by him as a way to internalize objects and thus to acquire desired qualities. The consciously admitted reason for a homosexual relationship with a man he expressed thus: "It is a way to make his handsomeness and virility a part of me—we would become one—I could never choose anybody inferior to myself—it is the same between a man and a woman, but I feel I would not want to incorporate a woman—"

However, fears of cancer appeared, which pointed to his introjection of his mother and his subsequently making her a target of his oral aggression. He complained that his shirt, hanging in her closet, took over her odor. It was evident that the internalization needs in the patient interfered with the libidinal investment in objects. The boy, because of his father's hostility toward him and passivity toward his mother, lacked a model for masculine identification. His frequent questioning of the female therapist as to whether she thought that he could become a great poet, be a real male, be successful and so forth, could not be answered in an effective way: his mother had always had a castrating attitude toward him.[9] On the other hand, her lack of respect and consideration for his father, together with her frequent exposure of her body to her son, played into his manifest delusions that she preferred him sexually to his father. Therefore the efforts of the female therapist, who intended to implement the plan to play an accepting mother figure, was offset on one side by the boy's panic reactions which the hostility engendered by his mother's rejection of his dependency needs and on the other side by his fears of incest. Both these anxieties made the transference situation unbearable. He began to break appointments, and when he came he would cry continuously that the female therapist did not help him. Yet, at the same time, in the interview material elements indicating the development of a nonrestitutional type of normal oedipal involvement (Flescher, 1953b) began to multiply: the patient assumed that his mother was a lesbian; at the same time he evidenced an unconscious fantasy that he himself was a girl and hoped to be loved as such by his mother. The "admired" boy of his homosexual fantasies was not only himself but also his father during a period when he had admired him for his magical power. On the surface, however, the patient continued to despise his father, accusing him of having intercourse with the mother in a "show-off" way in order to brag to his son of his sexual prowess. P. wished to turn Catholic because, "Catholics are not circumcised, and have longer penises." In September 1952 he was reading *The Well of Loneliness,* and subsequently kept up pregenital regression as a defense against castration.

By this time I had clarified for myself the possible advantages of a dual setting for P.M. In March 1953, I had the first interview with him. The focus was on his need for a "continuous refill," which, however, made him as "detestable" as his father. The patient feared to leave home because he might be attacked by others. After M2, P. told the female therapist how he regretted that his father was not a different man instead of the weakling he was. Though he had never dared to do so before, he submitted a poem to a teacher who could judge his work. Yet also fears were mobilized by the inclusion of a psychiatrist in his treatment on a regular basis. He wrote a poem about an "unsuspecting heart" that could be "trapped." He openly expressed concern that I might deprive him of the female therapist, in striking contrast with his previous complaints and frequent refusals, in the single setting,

---

[9] To a gift of a towel by the son, the mother responded disparagingly. This became the focal point of his accusations against her, which were certainly also related to her early and punitive training. (Toilet training began before he could sit up and was accomplished by ten months.)

to see the female therapist. His response was handled both directly and by increasing his contacts with the woman worker. In M4, he expressed lack of confidence in the encouraging attitude of the female worker. Simultaneously, the revenge motives that caused his staying at home and his not wishing to move out (though he was aware of how destructive the family situation was for him) came to the fore. In F5, the therapist noted a changed attitude toward greater security in the boy's posture, without relation to the nature of the material. For the first time he discussed, though still in a doubtful way, the possibility that his father might play a role in his homosexual fantasies. In F16, he considered with greater determination his plan to leave home, provided *he could count on the support of both his therapists*. Previously, he would not speak to his father, which was a magical way of denying his existence, but now he talked to him. In F20, he complained to the female worker that I was relating potency to sexuality, whereas he connected it with reproduction. If he ever should go out with girls, it would not be for sexual purposes, but only to talk with them. He said he knew that both of us, the female and the male therapist, were sharing their impressions about him. In close connection, he mentioned that in his family nobody really cared about him. He admitted for the first time that, while his mother always used to give him the feeling that he was better than his father and that she had a special interest in him which he enjoyed, he now could not disregard his father's possible anger against him. He felt that he could not go on living under a constant threat that his father could throw him out of the house. In the last interview, before the summer vacation, he communicated to me that, when I came back, I would find him living in the Residence Club.

My absence, however, led to a regression. He delayed leaving home, he told his parents about his homosexual wishes, he interpreted his mother's question, "What can I do for you?" as an offer of herself as a sexual object. There was a suicidal threat (which I handled by telephone through the female therapist) on the basis of anxieties increased by my absence and of the boy's acting out revenge motives against his parents because they were willing to let him go. It was shortly before my return that he finally moved away from home. During the subsequent nine alternate interviews, his sadistic fantasies against the peers whom he had long feared became open. He admitted having recently read a book by the Marquis de Sade. P.M. mentioned in his last interview that he had "jokingly" told a friend that he would like to crucify his roommate in the white space between two pictures on his wall. We remember that a few months previously he would write innumerable poems about Christ and his wish to be "one with Him." His sadistic fantasies which he had denied through projection onto others, but also enjoyed through masochistic defense, became subsequently much more direct and dramatic.

The patient's stomach rumbling disappeared after I interpreted it to him first superficially as an attempt to disrupt and ridicule serious and even solemn situations and then in terms of oral attack. The same thing happened with his stuttering. He participated in social gatherings in the Club, assumed the responsibilities of a student-teacher, and "stuck it out" with a very exacting, domineering supervisory female teacher. In M24, he brought in a dream in which he castrated a Club member whom he envied for his self-assurance; then he in turn was castrated by his supervisory teacher.

In conclusion, after eight years of psychotherapy of a severe borderline case which did not effect any personal or situational change in the patient, a few months of contacts—fourteen male and thirty-two female—in a dual setting succeeded in enabling the patient to leave home of his own accord and against all odds present in the family situation. He took over teaching responsibilities under emotionally straining conditions. After about sixty interviews, the patient left the Residence Club, lived alone on his own earnings as a teacher and had his first heterosexual experience. As the female member of the team had, because of family reasons, to restrict her professional activities, I decided to continue treatment on an individual basis. This case might be helpful in evaluating the suitability of the use of the dual setup on a temporary basis, in order to overcome an impasse in the standard treatment.

Case 3

Patient A.L., a twelve-year-old girl, suffered from attacks of loss of breath, from fears of being choked to death, of illness, noises, subways and school, and of being alone. She was diagnosed as anxiety hysteria. The fears had been aggravated by her father's death following a heart attack in her presence. From then on, she was unable to separate from her mother. She was treated by a female therapist without success from September 1952 to March 1953.

In April 1953, the decision was made to treat this child in a dual setting. The immediate goal was to counteract her strong masculine identification with her father, evident in her transference attitude toward the female worker in the single setup. After the second interview with the male worker, she told the female therapist that the day before she had traveled alone to the male worker's office for the first time since she had started treatment seven months ago. When she was sure that she was not losing the female therapist, she enjoyed seeing alternately two therapists. At the same time, she displayed also an obvious tendency to keep the workers apart, following the two major trends in the psychosexual development: exclusive possession of the mother and separation of the parents as a couple. She appeared upset when both members of the team jointly presented her with a birthday gift. (In the past, she would never go out with both parents together, but only with one or the other.[10]) In F6, she came dressed in a more feminine way, wearing cosmetics and earrings for the first time. She talked about her social activities with girls and boys. In F11, she discussed her dream of an epileptic man, concluding that it must be horrible for a man to lose control over himself or over his tongue. The fear of death by choking disappeared. During the following treatment, though previously avoiding any male company (at a certain point she had even had paranoically-tinged anxieties about men looking at her and following her), she began to speak of boy friends and of how much she liked her male teacher and even her dentist. Formerly objecting to school, feeling isolated and lonely, and also being disliked by students and teachers, she began to take her school attendance as a matter of course, became sociable and even popular. She accepted, without major emotional reaction, the onset of menstruation. Her need for her mother's presence disappeared progressively. She no longer feared to be alone at home. Although she had previously not mentioned her father since his death, her mother informed us that the girl herself initiated conversations at home about plans for her father's "unveiling" ceremony and brought up memories about him. Though she occasionally refused to come to one or the other therapist, her improvement continued strikingly. From April to July 1953, this patient had twelve alternate interviews (6F and 6M), from September 1953 to January 1954, twelve alternate interviews (7M and 5F).

Case 4

Patient E.F. was referred to me by a colleague. The young man had a borderline psychosis which had started five years previously, following a period of disordered sexual life. On his way home from military service, he "felt unreal," "did not know who he was," and developed obsessional ideas about killing himself. He feared that he was "disintegrating," and had the impression that people looked at him in a peculiar way. This state had developed after doubts had begun to torture him because his girl friend was neglectful in answering his letters. At the age of eighteen, when his brother died, the patient had felt responsible for his death. Short as the analysis was in this case, sufficient hostility was drained in the transference situation to make E. amenable to some insight into his ambivalence toward his dead brother, whose chronic illness had deprived him of his mother's attention. When the patient, after two and a half months of analysis, felt that he could stand on his own feet, I followed my experience in the therapy of psychotics (Flescher, 1953b) and did not try to insist that he continue. His interest in girls reappeared, he was more successful in his job. After a year, however, he came back and asked me if he could resume treatment. At this point, it was impossible for me to take him on. Besides, I had reason to assume that a female therapist would be more helpful to him in counteracting the influence which his rejecting mother had on him. The introjection of his mother, I felt, played an essential role in his fear of disintegration.

During the six months of treatment with the female therapist, E. improved further and resumed sexual relations with his previously mentioned girl friend. He abruptly broke the treatment because, as he recently revealed to me, the female therapist (who I knew was very proud of her "passivity" in therapy) did not react to his disclosure that he was about to lose his job. She was unaware that his apparently normal sexual adjustment covered very severe conflicts around unfulfilled dependency needs, and that, paradoxically as it may sound, his pregenital fixations had remained practically untouched. The patient resumed treatment with me in July 1953. He continued in his job and in his sexual relations with his girl friend, yet he was anxiety-ridden. He still feared that he would go crazy and that his jaws might suddenly lock. He tortured himself for his inability (which sometimes came out as a defiant unwillingness) to move away from home, where he was living with his mother and sister, whom he supported and to whom he related as if his father did not exist at all. A fantasy of his sitting on my lap was immediately followed by a wish to kill me, which reflected his difficulties around the survival of certain dependency needs involving his mother and a panic reaction because of the homosexual implication whenever he had to express these dependency needs in transference. He expressed fear of ejaculating during the session; then he visited a woman doctor, with whom he had the same fear but he "somehow felt relieved that the doctor was a female." He developed a strong sexual interest in this woman doctor; I concluded that he was about to displace the bulk of the maternal transference mobilized in the treatment into an area where he could act it out, and thus make the treatment relationship with me meaningless. This was confirmed by the circumstance that this sudden sexual interest in this female

physician developed while his long-standing and intimate relationship
with his girl friend was continuing.

By this time, I had already tested the dual setup in its practical
application. A female therapist, whom I had included since December
1953, saw the patient once a week while I saw him on a twice-a-week
basis. The immediate reaction of the patient was one of great relief.
He quickly abandoned the idea that I had diminished my contacts with
him because I was disinterested in him. He felt more comfortable in
criticizing me. He told both the female therapist and me about a dream
in which his parents discussed him, and he expressed his recognition
of having two people who cared about him. Commenting further on
his dream, he said that his parents never spoke to each other and that
he always felt guilty of having separated them since he came back
from military service. Subsequent material revealed the existence of
another, much more important period where the patient and his brother
had lived with their mother in a close union, in a sort of emotional
conspiracy against the father, whom they despised because he was a
bad provider and allegedly did not care for his family.

After F1, he told me that he intended to leave home and not cling
to his mother because she had actually never loved him. (In the past
he had rejected the idea that his fear of his mother's possible suicide
following his brother's death might have been determined by his resentment against her overinvolvement with this sibling.) He evidently was
drawing strength for the acceptance of this painful reality from having
found, in the female member of the dual team, an accepting mother
substitute. Following F2, he said that his girl friend was a wonderful
person and, though he was still unable to tell her that he really loved
her, he felt that one day he would do so. After F3, he spoke about a
strange coincidence: his father had shown concern about his possibly
having had difficulty with his car during a recent snow storm, and for
the first time E. noticed that he was able to respond with positive
feelings toward his father. He said he had had a wonderful week end
with his girl friend and had lived in a sort of "furlough" atmosphere
where every activity was meaningful and pleasurable. He burst out in
laughter (never before observed) when I formulated his castration
anxiety in a joking way. His past feelings toward a cousin who had
been important to him in his teens suddenly came back to him, and
he wondered why he now had conscious sexual fantasies about her
when at one time the very fact that she was separated from her husband
would have prevented him from paying her any attention. In the same
interview he spoke about a girl he had once known—a perfect woman
who had not aroused sexual desires in him. He told of how he had
gone through a period of trying to "purify" his relationship with his

girl friend, and admitted difficulties in combining great admiration with sexual pleasure in his relationship with any woman. In M3, the patient said, for the first time since I had been treating him, that he must let me know how much he appreciated my interest in him.

The most striking feature in this case was the ease with which the patient opened himself to the female therapist in the very first interview.

This patient, whose treatment has been concluded successfully after seventy-four interviews (he has kept a steady job and has married), gave me the opportunity to appreciate another asset of the dual setup: the change of the female therapist was accepted easily after a transitory and open expression of feelings of loss; the fact that the male member of the dual team did not leave safeguarded the emotional continuity of the treatment relationship.

CONCLUSION

The results with the dual method are very encouraging. They are not as impressive as those claimed by other authors using different techniques to shorten psychotherapy. Yet the newly proposed method will perhaps with time show itself to be more reliable in its results because of one basic advantage over any other therapeutic method: that is, it comes closest to the constellation of environmental influences which determine the destiny of the adult. The fact that the dual treatment is giving positive results with therapists differing in personality, degree of training and experience would speak in favor of the method as such.

Now a few comments on what we have observed:

Patients B.R. and E.F. reveal that exposure to the experience of *treatment by a male and a female therapist at separate periods* is therapeutically less meaningful than the *simultaneous alternate contact with a dual team.* In general, there were no difficulties in, and only brief preparation was necessary for, the inclusion of a second therapist in the treatment. This was no surprise to me, as it reflects the basic idea underlying my attempt. My conclusion is not contradicted by the fact that, with Patient P.M., anxieties emerged initially around possible loss of the first (female) therapist, which gave us important therapeutic clues.

My expectations that the inclusion of a second therapist would lead to fuller ventilation of the ambivalent feelings against one or the other therapist were realized in different cases in different degrees. I am unable at present to account for this finding.

The gathered material gave evidence that the dual setting exerts a sort of streamlining influence, not only upon the antithetical dependency and genital needs and the heterosexual and homosexual leanings, but also in the area of structural conflicts. We know that, on the oedipal level, the superego function is mostly related to the role of the parent of the opposite sex. The alternate treatment offers the patient an avenue toward greater clarification of the different roles that parents play as objects of emotional and physical needs and as restraining and censoring figures in the environment of the growing child.[11]

Then there is the long-debated question of constitutional bisexuality. Further experience with the dual method may show that conflicts arising in this area are decisively enhanced by environmental influences, and that they are reversible to a greater degree than our customary stress on the otherwise undeniable biological factor lets us assume. We all remember that Freud disagreed with Fliess when the latter ascribed to conflicts around bisexuality a major role in repression. The dual setting may shed additional light in this direction.

Future research may also show that the dual setting can even attack what Freud considered the unalterable "rock bottom" in analysis, that is, the masculine strivings in the female and the dread of passivity in the male. On the basis of the experience of reanalyzed cases, I have grounds for believing that the handling of masculine strivings in a woman follows different avenues

[11] The dual setting offers, for example, the possibility to implement therapeutically the experience of child analysts that the traumatic repercussions of a prohibition or threat can best be undone by the very parent who was responsible for it.

with a female therapist than with a male therapist, depending on the genetic history of the patient. To give a practical example: With a female patient whose masculine mother had wanted her daughter to be a male it might be difficult, if not impossible, to neutralize the disturbing factor in an individual analysis with a male therapist. If, conversely, it was the father's strong need to have a son that was genetically most decisive in promoting masculine identification in a female patient, it will be counteracted more speedily and effectively by a treatment experience with a male therapist. In both cases, the existence of the opposite member of the dual team is, for the presented reason, of invaluable help in the channeling of the treatment process in the right direction.

Moreover, there is the problem of the resolution of the transference. The famous Wolf-Man, analyzed twice by Freud, had years later a relapse of "a distinctly paranoiac character."[12] In commenting on this case, Freud (1937) reported that he twice thought he had analyzed the "unresolved residues of the transference." That it was not so was shown by the fact that those "residues" were still found by the female analyst to whom the case was finally referred. I wonder how the therapy would have proceeded if this patient had had a male and a female therapist concurrently. Freud also mentioned difficulties in handling negative transference that does not come to the fore. If there is a therapeutic method which promises to relieve us from the concern that a patient may leave us with an unrecognized transference (of whatever nature if may be), it is certainly the dual setting. Both the character and the degree of the emotional investment in one therapist cannot possibly escape the awareness of the other.

As has been shown elsewhere (Flescher, 1953a), the weight

---

[12] "The source of the new illness lies in undissolved residues of transference which, after fourteen years, gave foundation to the new illness" (Ruth Mack Brunswick, 1928). The author's evidently circular statement is probably influenced by the conflicted wish to emphasize that it was "a new illness."

of countertransference attitudes can make ineffective any intellectual planning of treatment in the individual setting. The dual
setting helps to put this disturbing factor under control. This is
strikingly illustrated by the consequence of the female therapist's relating Patient B.R.'s change in appearance to her coming
to see me. The assumption that countertransference phenomena
will be more easily grasped and controlled in the dual setting
than in standard therapy *even when done under supervision* has
been fully confirmed.[13] At a certain stage with Patient A.L., the
female therapist suggested closing the case because she felt that,
as the main symptoms had disappeared, the maximal improvement possible had been achieved. In the supervisory conference,
it became evident that she had fallen victim to a negative
countertransference response of reactive type (Flescher, 1953a),
because the girl currently preferred to have contacts with the
male therapist. It is easily to be assumed that such countertransference responses may greatly hinder a patient's maturational
progress in a single setup also, but with the difference that there
it is less easily detectable.

The dual setting may bring data to substantiate an assumption on the patient's need for his parents to be in harmony with
one another. This need is a precondition for the capacity to
unify the multiple instinctual aims that are directed with changing emphasis and in temporal succession first on one and then

[13] In reporting an interview with Patient E.F., the female therapist made
a slip. Instead of writing, "he talked about his girl friend," she wrote, "he
talked *out* his girl friend," and then corrected her error. I learned shortly
afterward that, in the interview, the patient spoke to the therapist about
the enjoyable week end spent with his girl friend, whereupon she, the
therapist, asked him if he had really enjoyed it. The patient expressed to
me his bewilderment that she had doubted his statement. I still considered
the possibility that the other therapist had aimed at uncovering his underlying discontent, but the fact that her report on this interview entirely
omitted the incident spoke for the intervention of countertransference. A
discussion of her apparently "reactive" countertransference helped us both
to bring it under control. In the dual setting we can thus study those very
factors which, in parents, interfere with the extra-familial involvement of
their children (Flescher, 1951a).

on the other parent. Perhaps this precondition may also be decisive in counteracting the inclination to exaggerate ambivalence which my previous research has shown to be inherent in the unfavorable "primary constellation" of the child (Flescher, 1951a).

My expectation that there would not be major complaints about confusing opinions or interpretations has been fulfilled. Evidently the emotional importance of having two therapists of different sex overshadows the necessity for finding absolute consistency and flawless logic in the therapist.

It is well known that the rule requiring the therapist to present himself to the patient as a sort of "blank screen," so that the patient's lack of information about the therapist may promote unrestrained display of his projections, also has its drawbacks. Experience shows that actual knowledge about the therapist's familial and professional status often has a decisively reassuring influence on the patient. The repercussions, for example, on the development of a child exposed to the seductive influence of a single parent in the permanent or prolonged absence of the second parent are familiar to every child psychiatrist and analyst. In this regard, the dual setting creates a frame of reference which definitely acts as an anxiety-reducing factor. This I have seen in all the cases which have undergone this type of therapeutic experience.

I do not believe in therapeutic miracles. The changes which have been obtained seem to me disproportionately great in relation to the degree of interpretive handling of the defenses and to the increase of the patient's insight. It may be that the dual setting may teach us that the relationship factor in the theory of psychoanalytic treatment has been neglected at the expense of the techniques of handling resistances, defenses, and so forth. But I am uncertain whether the deeper personality changes which assure us that the patient's improvement or cure will withstand subsequent emotional strain can be obtained by shortcut procedures. As some patients are still in treatment, the question of whether the favorable changes imply "transference improvements" cannot be answered.[14] But it is fair to say that they are more striking in intensity than those observed in treatment by a single therapist and involving the same number of contacts. The exception could be made that what we achieve in dual treatment is, if not identical, similar to what is known as "flight into reality." Patient B.R., who improved strikingly without increased insight, might support such an assumption. Even if it would be so—if I had to choose between the reality of a girl who brutally attacks and bites her mother and who, because of her paranoiac acting out with the individual therapist is on the verge of hospitalization, and the "flight into reality" through her merely superficial adaptation to objects and tasks—it is easy to guess what my choice would be.

In the more than three years during which the dual method has been applied in a total of twelve cases, I had the opportunity to verify whether this setup allowed for the appearance of superficial material only. Experience unequivocally proved, on the contrary, that the *anxiety-reducing* influence of the dual method favored the surrendering of material from deeply regressed levels. I shall give here only one illustration from the case A.B. (not reported here):

During this week he had the thought of wanting to dip his hand into the blood of a frog and to sing to himself right after that. "That means I established dominance over my father by dipping my hand in the blood." He felt elated when he dipped his hand into the frog blood. He had previously dipped his hand in the dried blood of the parakeet and felt that it was "incomplete" because the blood was dry. Right after that, he went into the kitchen to see if there was raw meat in the refrigerator so that he could touch and feel fresh blood. The meat was there but no blood, but he touched it anyway and licked his finger.

[14] During the intervening years additional experience was gained. Several cases have been closed and the therapeutic success has been maintained. In the case of B.R., the patient has remained for three years in satisfactory relationship with her boy friend and has made headway in her career as office worker without any further psychological help.

He didn't like the taste, it was salty, he felt a little sick because it tasted miserable. "But I thought of how I finally had been able to do it. I always thought of myself as hanging at the bottom of a pit or at the end of a ladder and barely holding on—I felt stuck in the middle of nowhere—and I never wanted to fall or be completely isolated, or rebound into a mental hospital or insanity—but I could not climb up and this touching the blood seemed a step in the right direction, toward becoming mature. Touching the blood was part of the long road back, or, rather, long road up the ladder—out of the pit—getting away out of personal contact, with my mother, the road being the means of traveling somewhere." (In a different voice and more directed toward me) "I told you about the time my mother told me about menstruation and since then I could not stand blood."

It is worth mentioning that this patient, who had been treated without any success by one therapist for three years for stuttering had after thirty-eight interviews in dual therapy lost his speech defect and has since initiated heterosexual activity. He has since successfully completed his academic training, obtained steady work in his profession, and has married. In addition, he was able to accept realistically the marriage of his sister, as well as the remarriage of his widowed mother. It was at this point that dual therapy was changed to individual therapy as a preparation for closing the case.

I cannot exclude the possibility that the dual setup will appear to be of major value only when the treatment is confined to infrequent contacts, where the goals of therapy are usually considered to be limited. On the other hand, increased experience with the new technique may show that at the end of even an intensive therapy in a single setting, the patient may benefit from exposure to the dual experience. As the transference and countertransference situations may be advantageously checked before discontinuation of treatment, the impression is justified that many so-called "relapses" may be prevented by this means. Space limitations prevent my discussing many other valuable data derived from my experiment. They will be presented in a larger publication on the same topic. The enrichment of our experience may lead to a more differential application of this method according to the pathology of our patients. It will also be of value in clarifying some of the technical problems of the standard analytic therapy.

In conclusion, I believe that the results hitherto obtained are sufficiently encouraging to warrant the application of the proposed technique on a broader scale. I would be inclined, at this stage of testing, at least to recommend dual therapy in any case in which traditional psychotherapy has failed, provided that those who intend to apply it have absorbed the theoretical foundations of this method and are able to carry out their basic implications.

I wish to thank Mrs. Lillian Sibulkin, Miss Naomi Grossman, Miss Helen White and Mrs. Rose Singer, all at the time of writing on the staff of the Madeleine Borg Child Guidance Institute, for their sensitive collaboration in the project. I am also grateful to Herschel Alt, Executive Director of the Jewish Board of Guardians and Mrs. Bettina Lehnert, Assistant Borough Supervisor of the Madeleine Borg Child Guidance Institute, for their early and encouraging recognition of the potentialities of the proposed method.

BIBLIOGRAPHY

Alexander, F. (1952), Some Quantitative Aspects of the Psychoanalytic Technique. Read at the Midwinter Meeting of the American Psychoanalytic Association, New York.

Brunswick, R. M. (1928), A Supplement to Freud's "History of an Infantile Neurosis." *Int. J. Psa., 9.*

Bychowski, G. (1950), Therapy of the Weak Ego. *Am. J. Psychiat., 4.*

Fenichel, O. (1939), Problems of Psychoanalytic Technique, Parts I-V. *Psa. Quart., 7-8.*

Flescher, J. (1941), Die "analogiemässige Gleichsetzung" als Fehlerquelle in der psychoanalytischen Forschungsarbeit. *Schweiz. Arch. Neurol. & Psychiat., 46.*

—— (1951a), *Mental Health and the Prevention of Neurosis.* New York: Liveright.

—— (1951b), Contribution to a Physioanalytical Study on Projection and Introjection. *Psa. Rev., 38.*

—— (1953a), On Different Types of Countertransference. *Int. J. Group Psychother., 3.*

—— (1953b), The "Primary Constellation" in the Structure and Treatment of Psychoses. *Psa. Rev., 40.*

—— (1955), A Dualistic Viewpoint on Anxiety. *J. Am. Psa. Assn., 3.*

Freud, A. (1928), *The Technique of Child Analysis.* New York: Nervous and Mental Disease Publishing Co.

Freud, S. (1904), On Psychotherapy. *Collected Papers, 1.* London: Hogarth Press, 1924.

—— (1910a), Observations on "Wild" Psycho-Analysis. *Collected Papers, 2.* London: Hogarth Press, 1924.

—— (1910b), The Future Prospects of Psycho-Analytic Therapy. *Collected Papers, 2.* London: Hogarth Press, 1924.

—— (1912), Recommendations for Physicians on the Psycho-Analytic Method of Treatment. *Collected Papers, 2.* London: Hogarth Press, 1924.

—— (1913), Further Recommendations in the Technique of Psycho-Analysis. *Collected Papers, 2.* London: Hogarth Press, 1924.

—— (1919), Turnings in the Ways of Psycho-Analytic Therapy. *Collected Papers, 2.* London: Hogarth Press, 1924.

—— (1937), Analysis Terminable and Interminable. *Int. J. Psa., 18.*

—— (1938), Constructions in Analysis. *Int. J. Psa., 19.*

Fromm-Reichmann, F. (1939), Transference Problems in Schizophrenics. *Psa. Quart., 8.*

Glover, E. (1926), A "Technical" Form of Resistance. *Int. J. Psa., 7.*

—— (1928), Lectures on Technique in Psycho-Analysis. *Int. J. Psa., 9.*

—— (1937), Symposium on the Theory of Therapeutic Results of Psycho-Analysis. *Int. J. Psa., 18.*

Klein, M. (1932), *The Psychoanalysis of Children.* London: Hogarth Press.

Loewenstein, R. M. (1937), Bemerkungen zur Theorie des Therapeutischen Vorganges der Psychoanalyse. *Int. Zeitschr. Psa., 23.*

Lorand, S. (1946), *Technique of Psychoanalytic Therapy,* New York: International Universities Press.

Oberndorf, C. P. (1942), Results with Psychoanalytic Therapy. *Am. J. Psychiat., 99.*

Reik, T. (1933), New Ways in Psychoanalytic Technique. *Int. J. Psa., 14.*

Sterba, R. (1940), The Dynamics of the Dissolution of the Transference Resistance. *Psa. Quart., 9.*

SOME ASPECTS OF A TRIPLE

3   RELATION: ACTIVITY GROUP—

GROUP THERAPIST—SUPERVISOR

Leslie Rosenthal

SUPERVISION IN ALL forms of psychotherapy involves a tripartite relation among client or group, therapist and supervisor. The therapist in the role of symbolic parent faces the impact of the whole range of human feeling in his treatment contacts; in the role of supervisee he in turn encounters authority and symbolic parenthood in the person of the supervisor. The supervisor is confronted with the repercussions in the therapist of the latter's emotional encounter with clients—a complex of feelings induced by client demands, hostilities, resistance, therapeutic progress, impasse or regression. Blended in this amalgam are, in addition, the therapist's own reaction patterns toward authority, judgment, praise and criticism of his performances.

The supervisor, for his part, brings to the supervisory conference an admixture of reactions toward the assumption of authority and varied needs for expressions of approval, admiration, confidence, compliance and dependency from the supervisee.

These emotional threads would seem to be part of the total fabric of the therapist-supervisor relation in all psychotherapy. Because it involves collective rather than unilateral therapeutic relations and because of its specialized setting, activity group therapy makes particular demands upon the therapist and thus brings certain patterns and problems to the supervisory process. It is the intent here to identify some of the prevailing themes and recurrent patterns in the interactive trinity of group-therapist-supervisor.

The group concurrently offers certain gratifications for the therapist and imposes certain frustrations. Through the establishment of his relation with a symbolic family, his "social hunger" (Slavson, 1943) and needs for parenthood can attain a partial satisfaction. The manifold opportunities to be giving— with food, materials, help, support and encouragement—may partially accommodate his desires to be a beneficent parental figure.

Yet, the very existence of the group automatically delimits the therapist's freedom to interact with any one of its members. A continued display of excessive interest in one child by the therapist would inevitably bring down the wrath of the group upon the preferred sibling. Conversely, rejection of one of its members by the therapist may unite the "family" in hostility against the parental figure. The defined role of the activity group therapist (Slavson, 1943) with its emphasis on passivity and neutrality further limits his interactive potential with the group.

It is this background of theoretically defined role, physical presence of group and personality of therapist from which emerges a recurrent theme in the group-therapist-supervisor triad: the therapist's wishes for greater intimacy and closer contact with the group or with one of its members. According to the unique variants of the specific situation, these wishes may jibe with those of the group or may be directly counter to group members' current needs for independence and emotional distance from the therapist.

Of four members present at one activity group session, three were withdrawn and passive to varying degrees while the fourth was an outgoing and active personality. The three withdrawn members remained quietly rooted at the refreshment table throughout most of the session in apparent ease and comfort. They obviously derived support from each other for their contemporary needs for avoidance of activity and insulation from the therapist. The fourth group member became enthusiastically immersed in a crafts project and with apparent pride intermittently displayed the project to the therapist.

In the ensuing supervisory conference the therapist emotionally demanded additional members for the group so that it could attain a proper balance. At the same time the therapist expressed strong sympathy for the outgoing youngster and voiced strong concern that "this child did not have anyone to relate to" at this session. At the following group session, two of the withdrawn children read comics during the refreshment period (testing the therapist's acceptance and permissiveness as well as expressing their anxieties around too close social contact). A more socially active member addressed a comment to the group which was not responded to verbally by the two socially fearful children. At this point, the therapist said to the active child, "You seem to be competing with the comic books."

The foregoing sequence would appear to suggest that those children whose current emotional needs were those of passivity, self-containment and social nonachievement exerted a significant impact upon the therapist. This influence was most pronounced when, due to the vagaries of individual attendances, the withdrawn members constituted a numerically dominant subgroup and made for two sessions in which there was lessened opportunity for intimacy between therapist and group. The therapist's intensity in presenting that one outgoing youngster had "no one to relate to" suggests that this represented the adult's own feelings (deprivation) in the situation.

In this specific incident the supervisor functioned by going over the history of the most withdrawn group member with the therapist. This procedure objectively highlighted certain facts: the child had been force-fed and constantly pressured to undertake social responsibilities before attainment of emotional readiness to do so. The therapist then readily perceived that the client at this point was not yet capable of assimilating the therapist's givingness and warmth, was not yet ready to partake of the therapist's inherent responsiveness (food). The gratifying aspects for this lonely client of being able to come together

with peers without attendant demands for further social participation and achievement were also touched on by the supervisor.

In an earlier publication (Rosenthal, 1953), the writer
touched on some of the situations inherent in activity group
therapy which readily evoke countertransference reactions; an
illustration offered was that of a therapist who, in describing
the group being quietly engaged in a project across the room,
recalled feeling "lonely and sort of helpless."

There undoubtedly are varied ways in which the supervisor
can address himself to such situations. What appears to be
crucial here, however, is his recognition of the inestimable
therapeutic value, when appropriately employed, of the therapist's capacities to relate, to respond with warmth and to convey
acceptance. The supervisor may be able to guide and rechannel
the therapist's innate capacities for relatedness—from a seductive, appealing and ingratiating client to a less attractive one
who may first need a supportive relationship with the adult prior
to sharing himself with the group. Or the therapist may be encouraged to relate himself more spontaneously to the group as
a whole. Such measures would proceed simultaneously with
helping the therapist attain a sharpened appreciation of the
therapeutic impact of the group itself upon its members and
the profound influence upon them of group approval or dis-
approval. Beginning therapists generally encounter some difficulty in comprehending the helpfulness of a policy of noninter-
vention. They may envision the therapeutic process primarily
in terms of their own direct and immediate impact upon each
child. Such a preconception is readily understandable if, as is
usually the case, the therapist has been previously trained in
the interpretive arena of individual casework practice.

A second major theme born of the relation of therapist to
activity group emerges from the therapist's perception of the
group potential for gross reactions. The element of contagion
(characteristic of all groups), the setting and the pivotal role
of the therapist in establishing the emotional climate—all combine to suggest to him the possibility of a mass reaction from

the group. There is thus a concrete anxiety that the group *might* erupt into aggressive or regressive unity; that it might become a mob. The new therapist particularly is prone to ascribe to the group those characteristics delineated by Le Bon in his classic study of the crowd. This anxiety is furthered by the permissive setting which the therapist establishes; thus in the very creation of the therapeutic atmosphere he may see himself rendered impotent to defend against "out of control" situations.

This anxiety constellation can influence and affect therapeutic management of situations within the group. One therapist, in an early contact with his group, rejected a request for a certain crafts material made in whining tones by an orally deprived member. He explained this handling as reflecting his desire "to avoid setting an example which the whole group could copy." The therapist was here confronted with the specter of an overwhelming group descent into infantile orality. It is possible that the therapist's reaction here was primarily based on countertransference toward an orally demanding client; however, even the use of a group reaction as a rationalization is significant.

In another situation, in the group's fourth session, one member acted provocatively and then left the room in the face of threats from two other children. Although no physical conflict of any kind had taken place, the therapist wished to contact the supervisor immediately to urge removal of the provocative member from the group. While the therapist's wishes to have a "happy family," unmarred by disharmony and conflict, contributed to his reaction, his primary concern revealed itself to be fear of an epidemic of aggressive-hostile feelings in which not only the offending member but the therapist too would be engulfed.

Here the supervisor functioned in accepting that this had been an upsetting session; in calmly predicting that there would be further testing out of aggressive feelings by the clients; in formulating with the therapist how this current and predictable behavior would be therapeutic for each of the children involved according to his unique dynamics. The impact of difficult clients upon the worker has been noted by Feldman (1956). She emphasizes the anxiety-allaying and tolerance-strengthening effect of the supervisor's calm acceptance of the worker's clients upon his own attitude toward them.

In helping the therapist to deal with this quite tangible and understandable anxiety, the supervisor can point to the necessity of the therapist protecting his status and stature in the eyes of the group; as the ultimate ego ideal, his person must be inviolable and should be protected, if necessary, with firm authority.[1] Related to this is the therapist's basic responsibility to intervene to re-establish controls when a member's or a "group's ego" has been overrun by his or "its" impulses. When the supervisor has oriented the therapist to these two aspects of role, the latter is then more assured that controls are available to him; indeed, that it is his responsibility to use them in emergency situations. With longer experience the therapist subsequently discovers that, because the group is balanced with diverse personalities (ranging from aggressive to passive, fearful and withdrawn clients), unanimous group behavior of the type he fears is quite rare.

A related though subsidiary theme deserves mention here, namely the anxiety-producing impact upon therapists of a group member's announced intention or request to bring a neighborhood friend to the group session. Some of the factors which appear to be active here are:

(1) Fear of the unknown child. Since the therapist has no prior knowledge of the visitor and no one has clinical responsibility for him, there is concern that he may prove to be excessively aggressive or regressive, may present severe problems of therapeutic management and may endanger the therapist's status.

[1] Because activity group therapy is experiential rather than interpretive treatment, direct aggression against the therapist cannot be discussed, interpreted and worked through; thus it cannot be permitted.

(2) Fear of a group reaction of resentment toward the "intruder" and of the possibility of other members imitatively or competitively also bringing friends.

(3) Resentment toward the group member involved. The wish to bring a friend is perceived as indirect criticism of the therapist, i.e., what the therapist is offering is insufficient to meet the child's needs.

It has been found helpful in the supervisory process to approach such a situation as another expression of the child's contemporary need; as such to be met with the same understanding as would his need to act out or to withdraw. The dynamics of the child and the contemporary group constellation will in turn give clues to the motivation involved. These may be one or a combination of the following: insecurity with his current group status and need for allies, a wish to enhance his prestige in his neighborhood by showing off the site of his gratification or even a wish to refer the friend to the agency. (On several occasions in interviews with group members, the writer has been told of a friend who "needs a club like this.") It is also indicated that the therapist be given assurance that if the visitor proves overly disruptive to group functioning, the situation will be appropriately handled through authority other than that of the therapist (thus preserving his role with the group).

The therapist's wishes for closer contact with group members and his concern with total group reactions of a certain nature and intensity have been discussed as factors which recurrently appear to influence enactment of his role. A third theme, overlapping, underlying and sometimes opposing the two cited, emerges. This is the therapist's search for equilibrium between the activity and passivity components of his role.

In his initial formulation of the role, Slavson (1943) describes the therapist as "a catalytic agent" in the process by which the client relates himself to the group; as "a synthesizing influence"; as one who "though neutral and usually passive, is the center around which the group constellates and to some degree also integrates." In addition, "he must become the ideal parent . . ." Slavson then acknowledges that "This anomalous position of the group therapist is not a simple one." A general impression, however, has developed of inactivity (combined with a nearly angelic tolerance!) as the major characteristic of the therapist's functioning. This conception may have been fostered by the widely circulated film on "Activity Group Therapy" which emphasizes the passive and group-peripheral aspects of the therapist's function. This partial misconception influences the beginning therapist's adaptation. Other factors, in addition to his basic personality, are the natural anxieties, doubts and feelings of indecision appropriate to entry into a new therapeutic endeavor. A further impetus toward restriction of activity can sometimes be found in the supervisor's cautioning admonition to the new therapist: "When in doubt, don't." He thus finds himself in conflict around the question of how far to extend himself toward the group and to what degree he should constrict his activity and submerge himself. The latter course is more frequently chosen since it offers greater safety. The totality of prior vague orientation to the role, confusion as to current expectations of him, and the initial situational anxiety may virtually immobilize the inexperienced therapist.

In practice, the presumed inactivity of the therapist is deceptive. While the two major facets of his theoretically defined role are neutrality and passivity, within this broad framework lies considerable scope for activity and for both clinically planned and spontaneous intervention. The fact that the group is composed of from six to eight diverse personalities in itself presupposes adaptations and refinements of the role in addressing the unique dynamics of each client. The therapist's respect for the schizoid client's need for emotional distance from objects will, of necessity, contrast with his responsiveness to the fatherless child hungrily seeking a paternal figure.

A major responsibility then confronting the supervisor is that of using himself as a catalyzing and synthesizing agent in the process of the therapist's orientation to role. An effective way of approaching this task is via the core problem and intrinsic need of the individual client on the level of his expressed behavior in the group. This approach can, for example, be made in such a universal situation as nonrecognition of the therapist by clients upon arrival at the meeting room. One child may thus ignore the therapist out of deeply entrenched hostility toward parental authority figures and to the adult world in general. The therapist's silent acceptance of this behavior is transmitted to the child as: "I respect your wish to avoid contact with me at this moment and I will not force you to relate to me. I have no need for you to like me and I shall not increase your guilt by thrusting my positive feeling upon your resentment." A second client may, upon arrival, also be silent and avert his glance from therapist. Here, however, totally divergent dynamics may be operative: deep affect hunger and yearning for warm relatedness may be held in check by feelings of worthlessness and fear of nonacceptance. In this instance a warm greeting from the therapist would hold obvious significance in conveying a message of acceptance and understanding to the child. In interactions such as these the therapist, given direction by the supervisor, can develop fluency in the use of dynamic, knowledgeable passivity or dynamic activity as called for.

Orientation of the therapist to role is then much more than a static adherence to a fixed attitude; rather, it encompasses the development of a readiness to respond with flexible, multiformed sensitivity to the multiple needs of the group.

Within this teaching and training framework the therapist can develop freedom and spontaneity in drawing upon his own unique personality and emotional resources in adapting to the group. He may then in the course of a single group session use various facets of himself: lend his ego (in the form of restraint or protection) to a child whose own ego is currently endangered; show a pervasive acceptance to the child striving doggedly to provoke his rejection; merge with the group in a moment of crisis when it needs the closeness and support of the parental figure; separate from the group—stand aside and allow it to grow away from him toward maturity. In this supple, variformed responsiveness to the differing and changing needs of his clients, he truly becomes the "ideal parent."

Several recurrent themes which emerge in the interwoven relation of activity group-therapist-supervisor have been identified as:

(1) The therapist's wishes for greater interpersonal contact in the interpersonal group arena
(2) The ultimate group potential for gross and total reaction and its influence upon the therapist
(3) The anomalies of the defined role of the therapist in activity group therapy and his quest for orientation and equilibrium within the role.

In these areas the supervisor is seen as functioning in aiding the therapist in the development (through sharpened understanding of intragroup dynamics) of emotional insulation against the impact of anxieties aroused by the group. In partnership, therapist and supervisor strive for refined sensitivities to the needs of the group and its members. The full richness of the therapist's potential to respond dynamically to these multiple needs is viewed as enhanced by the supervisor's respect for the uniqueness of the therapist's personality.

The selection of the three themes discussed in the preceding pages does not imply that they are dominant or unique in activity group therapy, in the parent field of group psychotherapy or in the over-all arena of psychotherapeutic endeavor. Therapists and supervisors in all forms of therapy are confronted with the problems and induced anxieties of transference and countertransference, of intense aggressive and regressive reactions by client, patient or group, and of proper definition of role. In presenting these three aspects as formed and molded by the climate of activity group therapy, the writer has been influenced by their universality and the consistency with which they have emerged in his experience as group therapist, supervisee and supervisor.

There are other varied facets of the group-therapist-supervisor relation equally valid and deserving of delineation and research. We have already considered the impact of certain group reactions upon the therapist and their overflow into the supervisory conference. The question can then be raised as to whether a therapist's current reaction or resistance to supervision may be dynamically similar to, and activated by, a resistance being currently employed by the group toward the therapist.

Another dynamic aspect worthy of exposition might be those internal and external forces which impel the therapist toward psychologically entering the group as a member and becoming a peer of his clients. Here, once again, we encounter the need for greater contact, but this time in the context of a sibling-like relation rather than on the parent-child plane. The presence of these impelling forces is revealed by the therapist's self-inclusion (on the children's level) in members' games and arts and crafts activities. Additional evidence is seen in a type of recording in which the therapist does not differentiate himself from the group, i.e., "We all continued working in this fashion until the close of the session." One may surmise that the group, and especially those of its members with pronounced oedipal rivalry, would overtly and subtly invite the adult to divest himself of his paternal status and join it as a peer.

Another, as yet uncharted, area in this specific milieu is in the influence of the therapist's unconscious upon the behavioral patterns of the group. Why do groups led by one therapist consistently act out considerable hostility in early sessions while others display a seeming outer harmony and much latent aggression? Why are some (male) therapists unconsciously perceived by the group as preoedipal mother figures while others are immediately the focus of transference toward the father figure? Given the interdependence of group, therapist and supervisor, would a competitive relation between the last two have any effect on the enactment of feelings of sibling rivalry within the group?

Another approach might examine the resistances in the supervisor to the release and development of the therapist's creativity. Some dynamic possibilities here may lie in the direction of the supervisor's need to have the therapist interact with the group in a restricted manner, i.e., as his deputy or extension. In his own work the writer has observed a tendency to overteach in his early contacts with new supervisees; feeling unsure of their acceptance, he has sought to prove himself and has thus offered much more than the therapist has been ready, emotionally and intellectually, to assimilate.

Experimentation with a group-supervisory procedure for activity group therapists offers another area of interest. Preliminary reports (Peltz, 1955; Winder, 1956) of this spreading practice of group supervision of a number of therapists are promising; they suggest that countertransference feelings are more readily recognized by therapists in a mutually supportive arena and that the therapists' own participation in the group sharpens their awareness of group-interactive patterns and problems.

It is felt that exploration of the above areas can contribute significantly to understanding and harmonious functioning in the interpersonal equation of group-group therapist-supervisor.

BIBLIOGRAPHY

Feldman, Y. (1950), The Teaching Aspect of Casework Supervision. *Soc. Casework, 31*:156.

Peltz, W. et al. (1955), A Group Method of Teaching Psychiatry to Medical Students. *Int. J. Group Psychother., 5*:270.

Rosenthal, L. (1953), Countertransference in Activity Group Therapy. *Int. J. Group Psychother., 3*:431.

Slavson, S. (1943), *An Introduction to Group Therapy.* New York: International Universities Press, 1952.

Winder, A. & Stieper, D. (1956), A Praepracticum Seminar in Group Psychotherapy. *Int. J. Group Psychother., 6*:410.

PART II

SPECIAL TECHNIQUES IN
CHILD GUIDANCE PRACTICE

In this group of papers will be found some contributions from the JBG's specialized residential and day care centers. The Hawthorne Cedar Knolls School, the oldest of these, is a residential treatment center for moderately disturbed children who can function in a cottage-type institution. It is large, complex and productive, and its staff have been turning their attention increasingly to the study and utilization of group processes and techniques. Mr. Goldsmith's paper demonstrates one aspect of this interest.

JBG's newest facility, the Linden Hill School, was designed to serve a group of severely disturbed adolescents who would ordinarily have required hospital care. The description by Mr. Scherer and his associates of the planning that went into Linden Hill is directed particularly to the attention of those who are in the process of dealing with similar problems in other communities.

Dr. Neubauer and his colleagues discuss here some aspects of the novel diagnostic approach employed in the Child Development Center, a day care center originally established by the New York Section of the National Council of Jewish Women with the professional collaboration of the Jewish Board of Guardians. Though now an independent agency, the Child Development Center retains its professional ties with the JBG as it continues to blaze new trails in the study of preschool children, both normal and pathological.

4 CLINICAL GROUP WORK IN A
RESIDENTIAL TREATMENT CENTER

Jerome M. Goldsmith

CLINICAL GROUP WORK represents a new professional dimension which we have added to the Hawthorne Cedar Knolls School program. While it is true that we have practiced group work at different levels for some time, it is only within recent years that we have established a well-defined clinical group work program integrated with therapy for certain of our children. We have had the opportunity to observe the possibilities of such a program in contributing to the advancement of the children's general treatment. The very nature of our children, our earlier failures and our increasing awareness that a segment of our program was inadequate forced us to formulate our goals and ideas around this group work program.

The Hawthorne Cedar Knolls School is a residential treatment center serving 200 children. A staff of 120 full-time people, some 40 part-time people, plus selected volunteers and over 200 acres of land make up the "psychogeography" of the environment. Many professional disciplines are represented in the staff: psychiatrists, psychologists, psychiatric social workers, teachers, group workers, cottage parents, plus the balance of our nonprofessional personnel who form an important part of the milieu, i.e., maintenance, kitchen, office workers, and others.

The children live in cottages with cottage parents and attend our own school where considerable effort has been expended to design educational programs tailored to serve children with emotional disorders. Each child is seen individually for psychotherapeutic interviews. The total milieu is conceived of as a living experience integrated with a child's need for gratification,

93

structure, etc., in an effort to advance the therapy of the child. In its simplest terms, our residential treatment institution restructures the reality of the child and integrates his living experiences concurrently with his individual therapy, where real people and real situations are sufficiently controlled and developed to meet the needs of these disturbed children. Our whole concept of residential handling is seen as an effort to undo pathology by constructing not only a benign environment, but one where planning yields a therapeutic design and atmosphere for the individual child.

At Hawthorne there are various kinds of groups: primarily, the cottage group where the children live and where a balance between structure and flexibility must be maintained so that the children can live together moderately successfully (essentially, conformity is demanded); the school group where structure again is important in providing a framework for learning and productivity, no matter how many individual curricula are developed; the community group which is rather amorphous but has some common denominators which go a long way toward developing the atmosphere and conditioning the children's concepts of treatment, self-examination and desire for change.

Then, there is the play group with which this paper is concerned. For several years Hawthorne had professionally trained group workers employed in its program who attempted to work with the children during their leisure-time periods. The group workers had the responsibility for the nonschool, noncottage time. In that time they were asked to develop programs and activities with these disturbed children which we hoped would stimulate some interests and give them opportunities for relaxation and enjoyment. Several sharp issues arose out of the experience of the group workers in our setting.

1. The group workers were not sufficiently aware of the depth of individual pathology of the children and were frequently manipulated and exploited to the disadvantage of the child's treatment.

2. No matter how successfully an activity began, nor how

much interest and excitement was generated initially, it dwindled in a matter of weeks. More frequently it was destroyed by the children themselves. Apathy and inertia deadened the program and finally discouraged and frustrated the group worker. The general permissiveness which the group worker brought to our setting was exploited by the children and resulted in attitudes and concepts about adults which stood out sharply from the rest of the total treatment setting.

3. Another interesting factor which emerged was that the group workers themselves were more comfortable in play situations with the children and rarely comfortable with the living demands when they came in contact with cottage life, or with the realities of the authoritative setting.

This experience occurred to us frequently enough to make us wonder whether there was some fundamental defect in the way in which group work was approached in our setting.

Faced with these problems, we set up a more carefully defined program for a segment of our population. We selected our junior cottages, involving about fifty-five boys between the ages of nine and thirteen. Friendship groups of six boys to a group were set up to meet twice weekly. Activities centered around play of various kinds. The children chose the boys they would most like to be with, and on that basis the groups were formed. The "rejects" whom no one wanted also formed a group. An interesting fact, which we hope to describe more fully at another time, is that the group which seemed the best, in terms of group goals and social development, was composed of the "rejects." The members of the other groups seemed to have chosen each other on the basis of reinforcing each other's pathology.

The person hired to develop this program was an individual who not only had had considerable experience in group work at community centers and camps, but also had considerable clinical knowledge and understanding of the emotional disturbances of children. He worked with the Junior Unit Supervisor, a member of the clinic responsible for the total treatment of the children in his unit. He was assigned the task of providing a leisure-time program afternoons, evenings and week ends for this group of boys. Our primary aim was to enrich the lives of the children sufficiently so that they might have fun and enjoy themselves. Helping them to feel that they belonged to smaller units in which their needs and feelings were considered, making it possible to achieve a better balance between self-expression and conformity, assisting them toward health through satisfying group experiences with an adult and each other and thereby generally enhancing the course of their therapy, were other anticipated by-products.

One of the differences between the group therapist's traditional role and that which emerges sharply in our setting is the therapist's need to be equipped with sound clinical understanding of individual problems and of the dynamics of emotional disorders. This understanding sensitizes our group workers to the awareness that the group has to be planfully composed so as to achieve a balance of children who can play together under at least minimal conditions. This knowledge makes them aware of the tremendous passivity, apathy and inertia of these children—characteristics which are symptomatic of the children's disturbances and reflect their relationships to adults and to each other. The dwindling and destruction of the group activities were then seen as a problem or result of the children's pathology which had to be interfered with. The children have little capacity to enjoy themselves and their problems soon intervene, not only to prevent the group from functioning, but also to prevent their own personal enjoyment.

The group worker's activity then becomes a direct therapeutic tool wherein he seizes the immediate opportunity to prevent this process of disorganization from taking place, thus enabling the children to continue the life of the group and their own personal involvement in it. To this extent, the group worker needs a great understanding of social dynamics and also of the individual pathology on which the group can be shattered if its mechanisms and operations are not dealt with successfully.

Another factor which influences the practice of the group

worker in our setting is that for our children, the white heat of the present is all-important and action and comments made at the moment may at times be of more value in advancing the child's emotional health than many hours of individual therapy. For most disturbed children, we have learned, there is no yesterday and there is no tomorrow. Incidents not dealt with at the time they occur may have little meaning to the child the next day.

The potential for advancing the therapy of the child is great. In these small groups the children are freer to behave and respond as they really are—for many, the defenses are lowered. This alone gives the worker greater opportunity to react to the child in a current conflict with a possibility of more healthful resolution. For this reason, awareness on the part of the group worker of the individual child and knowledge of where he stands in his individual therapy at the moment may make it possible for the worker to advance the therapy of the child by responding with purpose. In a sense, these play groups are the only voluntary groups within the institutional setting where the children are permitted virtually free play to their individual impulses.

If we identify social group work as a process, a method of working with people in groups, in which the professional understands and is aware of the interaction between the members and himself and is able to guide such interaction, then group work, as with our other disciplines, is modifiable or conditioned by the type of setting and the nature of its constituents. The group worker advances the therapy of the child through successful intervention into the pathological behavior of the child. His action helps the children to continue to function in voluntary groups and increases their capacity to behave as social beings and to experience a sense of personal enjoyment. This certainly adds another dimension to the treatment atmosphere of our setting and transforms a whole period of the children's time from vague notions about play activity to an important therapeutic period in the daily life of the child. While we are not going into such details of the clinical group work program as the formation of the groups, selection of the personnel and the criteria for grouping, we should like to outline very briefly the specific aims of this program and to describe the processes and some of the techniques employed.

Mr. Harold Esterson, Director of the Junior Clinical Group Work Program, has stated the aims more specifically as follows:

1. The enhancement of our diagnostic understanding, awareness of individual pathology and identification of positive ego areas in our children, through the planned observation of their social behavior and of their modes of interaction.

2. Promoting the evolution of group rules and of the capacity for individual conformity to group-imposed discipline.

3. Helping the children to develop awareness that specific events have sequences which block them from productivity, participation and satisfaction.

4. Helping the child to develop awareness of his defensive operations in response to experiences of adequacy, failure, success, closeness and anxiety-producing situations, and of his customary modes of behavior and of forming relationships.

5. Fostering the development of interpersonal relationships.

6. Assisting evolution of group activity and the satisfaction that goes with accomplishment.

Throughout all this the group worker is an active participant in that his role is planned, with planned intervention, planned comment or planned withdrawal. It is his own self-awareness, his evaluation of his own spontaneous reactions, his evaluation of the dynamics in the group situation at the particular moment and his understanding of the individual child's mode of operation which form the screen through which sift his activity and comments. The process itself must employ certain specific techniques on the part of the worker.

One of the major tools of the group worker is the "on-the-spot observation and interpretation." By interpretation we do not mean interpretation of unconscious conflicts or of deeply rooted unconscious mechanisms, but interpretation of the child's operational patterns as they appear in the group, and in terms of "here and now." The group leader does not sanction the distortions of behavior but points out why the child behaves in a certain way in the present situation. If this is not done, and the child continues his distortions, the group worker and the group experience are not helpful to him but serve to support the child's rationalizations for his behavior. The interpretation of the surface behavior breaks into the current pattern and prevents it from interfering with the pleasure of the group. For example:

1. Phil asked if we could play hide-and-seek. Mel and Jim eagerly agreed. Jack said suddenly, "Ah, why do you guys want to play that kid stuff for, who wants to run around like a bunch of silly idiots?" The worker, knowing that Jack had a sore foot and could not run, said, "Jack, because you can't play, you won't let the others enjoy themselves and play the games they want." The group, which had begun to question and reject the game as kid stuff and argue about who wanted to run around, were able to regroup and go on with the game. "Just because you have a sore foot and can't run, you do what you always do, *not* let the other guys enjoy themselves." Jack said, "Ah, I never have any fun, everybody picks on me." The group worker said, "You always say that, no matter what the occasion, if people don't want to do what you want. Your sore foot is no one's fault and no one is picking on you. You just have to blame everyone else for your problems. Why don't you try to be honest?" "O.K.," said Jack, "I'll sit this one out."

2. Paul's early contacts with the group were marked by distrust, hostility, feelings of being unrelated, and a certainty that no one could accept him, nor could he accept anyone else. During our first meeting, for example, he accused me of trying to hurt the boys, of being mean, and of not caring what happened to any of them. He fought with everyone in the group at one time or another, and especially with me. There were indications that he desperately wanted to relate to the group. At one point he fought with another boy who suggested that we ought to let him leave the group. During these first meetings it was also apparent that Paul put all relationships on a hostile exploitative level in which he inevitably became the underdog. He said he disliked the boys in the group, that he didn't want to play with them, and that they didn't mean anything to him. He could not participate in group activities, would not cooperate in any way, and did everything that he could to disrupt whatever activities we undertook. He did these things whenever he came to the group. However, this was not too often during our early contacts, for he missed three or four consecutive sessions. My approach to Paul during this time was to tell him that I wanted him to come to the group and to comment on what I thought was motivating him. For example, I said I thought he felt lonely and without a friend, that he thought that I was a mean adult who was out to hurt children, and that he really felt he wasn't too fond of himself, or anybody else. He thought the world a very unfriendly place where it was "dog eat dog," and "devil take the hindmost." Paul seemed to be very tense and unhappy during all of these meetings.

One of the first turning points in Paul's relationship to the group occurred during an early cook-out. When we were planning the meal the problem of Paul's being able to eat only kosher food was raised. The boys in the group spontaneously suggested that we buy kosher hot dogs. In addition, when we had the cook-out, the boys decided that since Paul could not eat the marshmallows we had, he should be given an extra hot dog. Following this, Paul never missed a meeting.

Another change in his behavior was that he no longer provoked fights. Once he became involved in our games, however, he was intensely competitive. His drive to win was so intense that it closed everything else out and made of games experiences loaded with frustration, anger (at himself, his teammates, the opponents), and misery. Every doubtful decision in a game became a *cause célèbre.* Paul became uncompromising, and would rather see the game broken up than concede the point. When his partner committed an error he would scream at him, and accuse him of giving the game away. He rarely smiled, or showed any sort of happy enthusiasm. Since Paul was the most poorly coordinated in the group, I continually asked him to play on my side. We reached a very dramatic climax during one meeting in which Paul and I were playing a game called "off the wall" against two other boys in the group. I had been pointing out to the boys this tendency to try to win at all costs, and their inability to enjoy the game, or anything else they did. During this game, whenever there were doubtful decisions I asked the boys who were closest to the ball to make the call. Since this occurred in the outfield, it was generally the opponents who had to make the call. It soon became a contest to see who could be the most honest. Paul reacted to this by at first pulling back, becoming silent, and observant. During the course of the game we had a chance to discuss how much more relaxed everyone seemed to be when playing the game became more important than winning the game. Following this, Paul's compromise was to become extremely honest in calling each play (and he did such unusual things as to remind the other team that his team had two outs and not one), and to berate me when I missed a ball. I ignored this berating and instead concentrated on the fact that Paul and I seemed to make a good team since I could field while he could hit. As the game continued Paul became caught up in the excitement until finally, on the way back to the cottage, I saw a genuine smile on his face as he discussed how close we had made the game (we lost by two runs). This began a period when loyalties in the group became realigned, with Paul moving from a "no prestige" member to a member who was accepted on equal terms.

I had noticed that after Paul went through a frightening experience, or felt particularly alone, he would stand and stare off into space, completely cut off from what was going on around him. My first approach was to point out to him that I recognized what was going on. I did this with such comments as: "You seem to be in a shell, Paul"; or "Paul, I have the feeling you've pulled away from us into a separate Paul." I then attacked the withdrawal directly. For example, during a basketball game an older boy hit Paul. After the boy left, Paul began moving around listlessly, and at times just stood stock-still. I shouted such things at him as, "You can't play basketball in a shell. . . . Come on out, Paul, it's safe for you now. . . . Paul, break that damn shell." If nothing else, the intensity of my shouts got through to him, for after several minutes as we brought the ball up court, Paul smiled and said, "I'm out, Warren." Shortly after this he said, "Come on, Warren, let's win." After the game I congratulated Paul on the quality of his play and, more important, on his fight to break the shell.

The group leader must be sensitive to the emergence of the healthy attempts of the individual and should encourage them in relation to others or to an activity. The following illustrates such an effort which helps the children to have fun.

3. The other fellows had begun playing "catch-a-fly and you're up." A discussion arose about how many strikes before you're out. Gary was pressing for a three-strike rule, directing this against Tommy because the other fellows were superior batters. I asked why they had to worry about strike-outs at all and Sandy said, "Because Gary will get more if Tommy strikes out." I asked if Tommy should lose his chance to learn

how to play better because Gary or someone else wanted to be up more times. Tim said, "O.K., we won't worry about strikes." Gary said they always had some rule about the number of strikes in this game. So I suggested having 700 strikes before a person would be considered a strike-out victim. They all laughed and Gary said, "O.K., anyone getting 700 strikes is out." Later on during the game the fellows showed a good deal of consideration of Tommy's inadequacy (he is, in reality, quite clumsy). At the same time Tommy was playing in a much more relaxed way and was really enjoying the game. On the way back to the cottage the fellows said they had all had a good time and they were getting good practice.

The worker's intervention in the group either through group confrontation or interpretation of individual behavior can be used to prevent setting up rules which are destructive to the individual child or which continue the competitiveness and the group "pecking order."

The choice of activity itself is very much related both to the children's fun and to its use by the youngsters either to isolate themselves from each other or to encourage interpersonal communication. The building of an underground hut or of a tree house may be chosen for its symbolic significance, expressing the group's need to hide from others and create its own special family unit. An activity can be designed for release, or, with alternate structure and flexibility, to give boundaries to the child or to his life-space as the situation indicates.

As stated above, the principal demand which this setting and the characteristics of the children make on the group worker is the need for greater knowledge of the individual group members and of their pathology. The group worker must be equipped to understand and recognize the various forms of group resistance, the evidences of anxiety, clinging mechanisms, the flight into activities and forms of group contagion. These have been fully described by Redl and Wineman (1951), Slavson (1943, 1946), Konopka (1949) and others.

There is need for broad clinical knowledge to identify disturbed behavior and encourage the healthy changes as they appear in the individual child. Keen understanding of the value of specific sublimatory experiences for meeting the demands of specific symptoms is required. There is need for recognition of the concept of total treatment and of the fact that the time allotment of the group worker is but a portion of the total treatment plan for the child. Actually, the clinical group worker requires the intensification of the same skills and knowledge described by Scheidlinger (1952) as basic to the equipment of all group workers.

In the Hawthorne setting, there are roughly four major disciplines comprising the treatment team. The clinicians pilot the treatment approach and conduct the individual psychotherapy. The child care people live with the children, perform the parental functions and give structure and framework to the child's daily living. The educators design the teaching program toward mastery of skills and achievement and essentially work in the ego areas. And, finally, the group workers are assigned the leisure-time program to enrich the children's living through enjoyable play and advance their therapy through successful group experiences.

Each member of the team is related to the general treatment approach and derives treatment orientation from the clinician. However, no member of the team is burdened by a prescription from the pilot, but each performs a specific function through his own specialized techniques and skills with responsibility for a time period in the child's life. Each discipline must function within the same philosophical framework governing the treatment approach of the entire setting.

The group worker has a contribution to make to the other disciplines through the refinement of professional observation of the behavior of children and their difficulties, with all that this implies in relation to increasing diagnostic understanding.

Contributions of clinical group work to the other disciplines working with children in groups are in the areas of methodology, understanding of group phenomena and techniques for handling extreme behavior. The group workers participate with the other team members as well as with the entire staff in creating the treatment atmosphere and attitudes which, in essence, form the therapeutic assault.

Weaving all of these specialized skills into a consistent treatment plan involves successful communication and integration. This is accomplished through many means: planned conferences with individual therapists, planned progress meetings in which the group worker participates fully, records of group sessions sent to the individual therapist, reading of the individual therapist's records by the group worker and many other formal and informal means of communication. These devices insure clarity of treatment direction and opportunity for frequent checks. They may serve to set up situations for support, to create anxiety or to continue along the same prescribed course. The essential element lies in the frequent exchange of information and "resetting of sights" with reference to the individual child in his present state.

We began this paper by describing our initial experience with group workers, which was not successful. This was apparently due to their limited clinical knowledge, their limited understanding of the nature of the disturbed child, and their inability to reconcile their group work concepts with the destructive pathology of these children and with the authoritative residential setting. After two years with the special program we have described, we saw a successful group work program with fun for the children, enhancement of their treatment and the stabilization of successful play groups on a continuing and voluntary basis. The activity was achieved with professional workers who possessed self-awareness and a conscious use of certain techniques and attitudes. As they formulated the attitudes and as we talked more actively with our nonprofessional child care people, it became apparent that our most successful cottage parents were using many of the techniques—interpretation, support of group attitudes, etc.—intuitively. They had achieved this knowledge through direct experience, supervision and success through trial-and-error methods. The implications of such a program for total residential treatment are enormous because the group worker through his formulations has produced material which is teachable and translatable to the child care people and to those living with children in groups. In this connection our most recent residential treatment project, the Linden Hill School, has utilized professionally trained group workers as child care counselors, performing the parental functions and yet using methods of handling aggression, withdrawal and the experiential aspects of daily living, with more self-awareness and with utilization of techniques similar or identical to the ones discussed throughout this paper. We have found that this has advanced the therapeutic contribution of the daily living experiences beyond those offered by a merely accepting environment.

We begin, then, to see group work, as modified in this setting, as a technique applicable to child care, cottage life, teaching or education, as well as to the leisure-time activity program which the group workers have historically staked out as their province. Certainly, modifications in technique are necessary and may have to yield to the treatment design calling for more structure or authority than in the voluntary play group. The possibility of evolving a residential treatment worker from the clinical group worker is an exciting one and the most promising in our search for the ideal residential treatment worker personnel.

Specifically, we see this group work program not as an ancillary service to the main course of therapy of the child nor as shoring up the major therapeutic structure which lies elsewhere, but as a specific therapeutic approach having its share of the child's time which must be met with a specific program, direction and performance. The program fits into our general residential treatment context and our concept of total treatment, which in essence recognizes no center of treatment except the child himself as the object of all therapeutic effort. One might reflect whether in this context this technique might not be labeled group therapy rather than clinical group work. To the extent that therapy means planned conscious approach designed to advance the health of the child, it might well be identified with group therapy.

However, it is not designed specifically to unravel the child's pathology nor to treat the specific symptomatology which might have brought him to the institution, but to prevent the individual pathology from hindering the child's enjoyment by destroying the group. Indirectly, therefore, by building up his strength and health, it does have very concrete therapeutic values. In this respect the program approach is concerned with social manifestations of the unconscious problems and conflicts.

Essentially, this is not group therapy but, more properly, therapeutic group work. The play situation cannot be isolated from the rest of the treatment-centered environment; to the extent that the group worker can summon sufficient skill and self-awareness, he can utilize his methods in the direct treatment of the child.

In our environment, the failure to weave the group work program successfully into our treatment pattern left a gap which canceled other helpful effort, or caused the program to succumb to the onslaught of the symptomatic behavior of the children. Our concern with the extent to which the illness of the children interfered with their enjoyment forced a therapeutic concern and developed a therapeutic approach in the groups. We now have had several years' experience with the same children where groups have continued on a successful, productive, voluntary and continuing basis. We have yet to realize the full fruit of the therapeutic values for the individual children involved.

BIBLIOGRAPHY

Bettelheim, B. (1950), *Love Is Not Enough*. Glencoe, Ill.: Free Press.
—— (1955), *Truants from Life*. Glencoe, Ill.: Free Press.
Cabral, A. & Bloom, M. (1954), A Description of a Newly Introduced Group Work Program in a Residential Treatment Setting—Haw-

thorne Cedar Knolls School. Submitted for Master's Thesis, New York School of Social Work, Columbia University.

Freud, S. (1922), *Group Psychology and the Analysis of the Ego*. London: Hogarth Press, 1948.

Konopka, G. (1949), *Therapeutic Group Work with Children*. Minneapolis: University of Minnesota Press.

—— (1954), *Group Work in the Institution*. New York: William Morrow & Co., pp. 51-155; 185-251.

Redl, F. & Wineman, D. (1951), *Children Who Hate*. Glencoe, Ill.: Free Press, pp. 122-137.

Scheidlinger, S. (1952), *Psychoanalysis of Group Behavior*. New York: Norton.

Schulze, S., Ed. (1951), *Creative Living in Children's Institutions*. New York: Association Press, pp. 35-50, 79-96, 97-116, 117-128.

Slavson, S. R. (1943), *An Introduction to Group Therapy*. New York: International Universities Press, 1952.

—— (1946), *Recreation and the Total Personality*. New York: Association Press, pp. 1-70, 86-141.

Sullivan, H. S. (1953), *The Interpersonal Theory of Psychiatry*. New York: Norton, pp. 217-296.

5 DESIGN OF A TREATMENT SETTING FOR ATYPICAL ADOLESCENTS

Marvin Scherer, Leonard Kornberg, Ed.D., Lloyd T. Delaney, Albert Hotkins, M.D., and *Kurt Salzinger, Ph.D.*

THE DESIGN OF a residential treatment setting is the result of many elements. Among these are the stated and unstated purposes of the institution, the auspices under which it is undertaken, and the philosophy and background of those planning it, the size and nature of the group of children to be treated, the kind of building or physical setting available, the number and qualifications of the staff available, the personalities as well as the ideas of the people administering it. To examine with any thoroughness the designing of an institution such as the Linden Hill School, one would have to go far back, to examine the whole history of institutional treatment, to consider the development of the Jewish Board of Guardians, the attitudes and predilections of its board members, the contributions of all those people who were influential in planning and initiating it, the reasons for the choice of our present staff from top to bottom. More particularly one would have to examine the whole body of experience, ideas, and attitudes regarding residential treatment accumulated over the years at the Hawthorne Cedar Knolls School, of which Linden Hill may be more accurately seen as an offspring rather than a sibling. Finally, one would have to describe the processes by which an organism such as Linden Hill develops from day to day, since the designing is not something which took place only before there were children and staff in our building, but rather something which is taking place now and from minute to minute of our living together at Linden Hill.

We must recognize then that we can speak here of only a few of the elements entering into the design of Linden Hill. Linden Hill has a capacity of twenty-six children, thirteen boys and thirteen girls. While the size of our group was conditioned by the building we had available for our use, it is, I believe, approximately the size we would have selected. Our program is carried out in one large building, which contains living quarters, school, clinic, and recreational rooms. For living purposes, the building is divided in half with separate living rooms and dining rooms for boys and girls as well as individual bedrooms. Our children range in age from twelve to sixteen, approximately. In general functioning, social maturity, etc., we have attempted to admit a group of children who are fairly homogeneous, that is, we do not have a junior and senior group. When we have admitted a twelve-year-old, it has been after careful consideration of his probable ability to live with and function as part of a group of children who are in the main chronologically older, and similar consideration has been given to the admission of children at the upper end of our age range. We have a staff of thirty full-time and part-time people. The child care staff, that is, the people who live with and care for the children in the home situation, total eight, and there are two counselors on duty with each group of thirteen children during all nonschool hours.

The children at Linden Hill come to us from courts, agencies, hospitals, private psychiatrists and parents. Those admitted are considered at intake to require a more protected and protective, a more tolerant, flexible, individualized and intensive program than is available in most residential treatment institutions, but not to require the protection and supervision of a hospital setting. Diagnostically they fall into the categories of schizophrenia, borderline psychosis, infantile personality, severe psychoneurosis and character neurosis. Included are some with known organic complications, where the organic problem is not seen as the basic element in the disturbance and where we feel that the child is accessible to treatment through primarily psychological methods. A very important consideration in our choice of population is our belief that children whose disturbance is shown primarily in extremely aggressive, delinquent and impulsive behavior require a different setting and program from that most suitable to children whose major symptoms are withdrawal, fearfulness, bizarreness, infantilism, and a tendency to lose contact with reality. We have selected to treat at Linden Hill the latter kinds of children and have not admitted the former group when we have been able to evaluate them as such at intake. This is not to say, of course, that our children do not show serious behavior disorders, that they do not have severe temper tantrums, exhibit marked hostility, negativism and destructiveness. They are, however, substantially different as a group from the delinquent and socially aggressive adolescents who form a large part of the population at Hawthorne Cedar Knolls.

Two of the first children admitted to Linden Hill were Lucy and Tommy. Lucy was admitted at the age of sixteen from a mental hospital. She had been hospitalized because of severe regressive behavior. Lucy walked on all fours and made animal-like noises. She had violent temper tantrums, destroyed furniture, attacked her mother and stepfather with knives, and exhibited herself in the nude. She had a severe speech disorder, her articulation resembling that of a two-year-old. She was extremely self-conscious and fearful with other children, unable to function socially, and unable to care for herself in a manner remotely approaching the level of an adolescent girl. There was a background of divorce and remarriage when Lucy was a small child with Lucy living with her mother and stepfather, and with most of her aggression directed toward her mother.

Tommy was admitted to Linden Hill at the age of fourteen. This is a boy who had shown a lifelong fear of other children, had never been able to play, could not be kept in a community school where he was a constant butt of other boys' aggression and teasing. In school he had frequent episodes of screaming, running around, and complete disorganization in which he seemed to lose contact with reality. For a long time Tommy had

not left his home except to go to school or synagogue. He oc-
cupied himself with his intense interest in maps, radio and
television programs, schedules and timetables and religious ob-
servances. He had, apparently, never had any social experience.
He lived with his mother and a maternal uncle from the time
of his parents' separation when he was two and a half.

Most of our children show similar tendencies to respond to
pressures by severely regressive, disorganized and infantile behavior, extreme social inadequacy, withdrawal from peers, and
generally restricted functioning. Some have mild delusional
ideas or hallucinatory experiences. Some have severely handi-
capping phobias or compulsive and ritualistic behavior. Others
show a constant restlessness, anxiety, and tendency to panic or
hysteria.

In designing a therapeutic setting for these children, our first
concern had to be to provide for them a living situation sufficiently free of pressures, threats and demands that they could
exist with some feeling of comfort and not have so great a
need to resort to regressive, disorganized and panicky behavior.
This involves a great many things which together make up the
general atmosphere and "feel" of Linden Hill. To enable a
child like Tommy to live in a group situation in the same building with other children twenty-four hours a day means that
there must be enough of the right kind of adults to serve as a
buffer or insulation between him and the other children. It
means providing for him opportunities to wander around alone,
to talk to an adult when he needs to. It means allowing him
to make lists of radio programs, to study and to become our
expert on timetables, to examine and to type staff schedules in
advance, to discuss the menus and examine the food before it is
served. It means giving permission to Tommy to retain, while
he so desperately needs them, whatever defenses he has been
able to develop for himself, helping him to strengthen some of
them and to direct others into more useful and satisfying chan-
nels. With Lucy, at the beginning it meant accepting her as a
much younger child to the extent that she showed the need to

be treated as such. It meant in the living situation that a counselor spent hours with her in her room going over her clothes, helping her choose what she was going to wear, planning purchases, helping her to put away her clothes and keep her cabinet in order. It meant responding to her feelings of inadequacy with other girls by constant comfort and reassurance from counselors rather than making demands and giving indications of disappointment or misdirected encouragement to tackle situations which she would not be able to handle. It meant, above all, attempting to recruit a staff who could not only accept these children with their pathology, but also find satisfaction in working with them, and have the patience not to demand more movement than they are capable of making.

A complementary consideration in our design at Linden Hill is our concern with helping our children gradually to give up infantile and regressive behavior and motivating them to higher levels of functioning. At the beginning our efforts are directed to learning under what conditions, in response to what stimuli, or in the satisfaction of what needs the particular behavior appears. Tommy's strange temper tantrums in which he grunts, roars, and screams and becomes red-faced, inarticulate, kicks the wall, and cries repeatedly, "Get out of here! Get out of here!" we have found are often related to food, often to a minor frustration of which we have been unaware, often to some change, small or large, in the usual order of things, or to some anticipated disappointment of a desire which Tommy may not yet have expressed to anyone. At other times they are in direct response to teasing or aggression from other children. For some time, when we were able to recognize the cause of a particular tantrum early in its development, we would try to meet Tommy's need quickly, either in actuality or through reassurance. Gradually, however, we attempted to help Tommy understand and accept reality. As we felt that Tommy was beginning to see us as people who could be trusted to have some concern about his welfare, we have tended more and more to substitute for this immediate need gratification a request that he submit his dissatisfaction to rational discussion, recognizing every indication of an increased ability on his part to do so through words, attitudes or concrete rewards.

With Lucy we found that any situation in which she felt at all rejected or disapproved of would produce crying, depression, complaints of total inadequacy or protests of unfairness, rage, and generally infantile behavior. For a long time such frustrations were frequent and inevitable in Lucy's living at Linden Hill. The efforts of Lucy's counselors were directed toward gradually helping her to reconcile her needs with the demands of socialization. They had to find ways to shape situations in which she could be encouraged to make legitimate demands and to attempt limited entries into competitive situations; where she had opportunities to get what she wanted and to achieve some degree of acceptance and status. With this help Lucy was able, a few months ago, to have a boy friend, although he was one of the most socially inadequate and lowest in status of our boys, and then to recognize the limited satisfaction this gave her and to move to giving him up as not coming up to her legitimate expectations for herself. Thus, it is our attempt to provide for each child the satisfaction and conditions which will enable him to move to more effective handling of reality and to provide the incentive by increasing our demands in step with the increase of his capacities, and by recognizing and rewarding any movement.

Another significant element in the design of Linden Hill, and one whose importance is impressed upon us more and more as we get to know our children better, is the structure of living into which the children are drawn. For most of them the simple, concrete and routinized organization of living at Linden Hill is the basic thing to which they originally relate and around which they can move toward improved inner organization. For most of them this seems for some time more important than their relationship with any particular adult. Life as a whole has been confusing, discouraging, and disorganizing to these children. They have seen it as too complex, too demanding, and as serving only to emphasize their inadequacies. The simple chores of making beds, or cleaning a room, of setting a table—a program that is structured as to time and place, stimuli, expectations, rewards and punishments—provide them with a primary basis for directing their energies toward reality. As with the infant, these routines make life for our children more understandable and manageable. Performing the simple tasks which are within their powers permits the release of energies to deal with the external world with its accompanying satisfactions, and again we attempt gradually, as the child's capacities increase, to raise our expectations and enlarge the area and complexity of his functioning.

The primary role in carrying out these principles of our treatment design at Linden Hill is played by our child care workers or counselors. There is, of course, a great deal of overlapping of function among all the staff who have to do with the child. It is the counselor, however, who, in the closeness of his contact with the child, the basic nature of his responsibilities, and the variety of experiences he shares with the child, is the bearer of the therapeutic essence of the residential program. The recruiting, selection, training, and holding of specifically qualified child care staff is one of the major problems in administering a residential treatment program. The problem is intensified at Linden Hill by the kind of children we are treating. Those of you who have attempted the individual therapy of a borderline psychotic child may be able to imagine the overwhelming nature of living with a group of such children. The sudden and drastic changes in mood, the presence of thinking and feeling simultaneously at all levels of development, the shifting transferences, the difficulty in communication, the intensity and unpredictability of feelings and behavior, and the discouraging slowness of therapeutic movement—all these demand maturity, flexibility and resiliency of personality, in addition to the most sensitive and skillful use of oneself. In the belief that professional training, discipline and awareness should have much to contribute to effectiveness in child care, we have within each group at least one professional counselor helping to set the pattern of handling. Our concept of a professional counselor is one who comes with graduate training in the fields of casework, group work, or special education. In general, our other counselors are people with college training and future professional goals.

In defining the part that the counselor plays at Linden Hill, it should be mentioned that he does not in our design take over any of the functions of direct psychotherapy. While it is expected that the counselor will utilize the insights to be gained from clinical understanding and contribute to such understanding, his therapeutic impact on the child comes through relationships, attitudes, activities, and the use of himself in living experience. The counselor presents to the child, not primarily in a symbolic way or as a result of transference but concretely, nourishment, security, and protection from outer and inner dangers. Tommy is disturbed to some extent by any change in the environment, but even a minor deviation in the counselor's schedule will throw him into a panic, for a more basic threat is involved. Although the center as a whole may more properly be considered the parent substitutes, and individual relationships with other staff may be more significant with particular children, it is the counselor staff who most importantly personify the elements in the therapeutic design that touch the child most intimately and deeply.

The living situation, with the counselor and the living group, is for the child the closest parallel to the family situation and the area in which his feeling toward parents and siblings are most apt to be reactivated and expressed. Lucy's mother is an attractive, narcissistic woman who, out of competitive and destructive feeling, had constantly pressed upon Lucy grown-up standards, pointing out her inadequacies in appearance, dress and social behavior, and comparing her unfavorably with other girls. As her counselor worked with the girl, sewed and cooked with her, helped her with her makeup and clothes in an encouraging and supportive way, Lucy began to talk with her therapist about her competitive and hostile feelings toward her mother, which had caused her to resist any movement toward growing up before. This became possible after a long period in which Lucy's infantile needs were accepted and catered to by the counselor.

Because of the degree of disorganization of our children and the fact that many of their problems are related to early developmental levels, the basic activities of the living situation—eating, sleeping, bathing—assume great importance. We know that for many of our children it is too late to undo more than partially the damage resulting from early deprivation or traumata. While the experience of direct therapy and the more sublimated satisfactions of school, group work and recreation have their own benefits to contribute to our children, it is the intimate and repeated experiences of daily living, we believe, that can best provide this basic re-education. For this reason, a great deal of time and attention is given to the child by the counselor around these activities. At the same time, our efforts are directed toward drawing the child into the structure of the living program so that these activities can gradually lose their earlier associations and become the simple daily routines of the more mature ego.

In addition to the experience of a therapeutically designed living program, all of our children receive individual psychotherapy, most being seen at least twice a week. We shall not attempt here any detailed description of the techniques or processes of the individual therapy. In general they are not essentially different from those practiced elsewhere in the Jewish Board of Guardians. At Linden Hill, to a greater degree than in most residential treatment settings because of its small size and the opportunities for communication among the staff, the therapist has available to him the observations of the child care staff as well as opportunities to make his own observations of the child in other roles, activities and relationships. This affords rich clinical material to sharpen his insights and to be used appropriately in the therapeutic sessions. The relationship between what goes on in the therapy and the child's daily functioning is often apparent, at times through his response to a particular interview which may be acted out or expressed to another staff member. On the other hand, the insights growing out of the therapist's work with the child are available to supplement those of other staff in their understanding of the child's behavior and planning of his handling.

Thus the experience, observations, understanding and insights of therapist and child care staff become the basis for reaching some common understanding of the child. This understanding becomes in turn the basis for each staff member's work with the child, utilized in the appropriate setting and form. The recognition of Tommy's overwhelming oral needs led to the counselor's having him help prepare breakfast and receive special treats, the teacher and group worker utilizing food as a means of drawing Tommy into classroom and recreational activities, and the therapist's spending the interviewing time in eating with the boy. At the same time, the need to help Tommy to learn to accept the demands of reality and socialization was approached by the counselor's insisting that Tommy wait for the other boys before eating, the group worker's having Tommy prepare his food with another boy, and the teacher's having Tommy serve snacks to the class. The recognition by the staff that there had been some increase in Tommy's ability to tolerate tension was a cue to the therapist to diminish the eating activity and attempt more formal interviewing with the youngster.

The psychiatric staff function in every phase of the program and lend their special skills and knowledge of personality structure to the determination of general policy and over-all program, as well as the individual patient's adaptation to that program. Each case is seen by the chief psychiatrist prior to admission, so that the tentative total treatment plan can immediately be instituted on admission. Regularly thereafter, the supervising psychiatrist meets with the individual therapist to review treatment progress. From his dynamic understanding of the case, the psychiatrist is then able to help staff to transmit these particular findings into the daily living treatment of the youngster, with the goal of replacing pathologic defenses with healthier ego function. This is accomplished in the course of regular conferences with the administrative, the teaching, group activities and counselor staffs.

A significant part of our design at Linden Hill is the school program. Because of the wide scatter in ability and interest of our youngsters, their extreme range of reading ability, numbers skill and informational level, the problem of organizing class-room instruction challenges one's ingenuity. To meet the dual needs of, on the one hand, the extreme difficulty our children have in functioning as members of a group, their self-absorption, their difficulty in giving their attention to assigned tasks, their need for limitless attention from adults, and their very restricted capacity for purposeful effort and, on the other hand, their need to be supported by external structure and organization, we have developed a system of having each child spend part of his day in what we call a "home room" and part of his day in "unit" classes.

In the home room, class assignments are individualized and according to interest. Here the class structure is fluid and informal, with the relationship between teacher and individual child. The home room is the workshop for a variety of performances and projects where the teacher is each child's support and consultant. Unit classes, however, are more formal in structure, with the focus on a common subject and with the teacher facing the group. Such a program, we find, provides a schedule of changes necessary to dispel tensions, modulates the teacher's role between that of a giving and demanding person. For children who have had predominantly unhappy experiences in school, who have been unable to conform or to achieve, this design seems to offer much. Lucy, for example, needs an extraordinary amount of warm assurance, personal attention, and organization by the teacher before she can apply herself to the difficult challenges which organized learning represents for her. Each morning in the home room Lucy begins school by writing something, a letter, a story, a poem. Her teacher must not only help her to spell certain words, correct the grammar, but she must listen to repeated readings, help her clarify her thoughts, help her put things in order, and produce something. This is not merely a job of turning out a piece of writing; it is a device to fortify Lucy with the reassurance she needs to tackle the more mature challenge of working in a unit class.

For Tommy, on the other hand, the home room is the dangerous place where he is on his own and not tied by an obvious structure. He spends his time there devising his own moorings, sometimes by doing homework for a unit class, sometimes by listing words compulsively, sometimes by reading a book or newspaper. All the while he is aware of happenings in the room, furtively watching the children or teacher, daring occasionally to say or do something which will bring him into contact with others. When he moves to a unit class the structure is given by the subject studied. Here he knows better where he is and what must be done. He has a chance to use his good abilities for abstraction, to get good marks, and compete successfully.

Thus the school, within its own special aim of developing our children's skills and giving them the educational tools with which to deal with reality, carries out the basic design of our milieu, that is, it attempts to take account of and meet the child at his level of growth and pathology while also helping him, through its organization and focus on object relationships, to move from infantile to more mature and socialized functioning. Again, just as with the counselor in the living situation, the teacher's personality, attitudes, and skills as well as the structure of the program itself and its moving current are the tools that are used. As much as the more usual learning of subject matter and technical skills, our children require a basic orientation to time and space; they need to learn the use of tools and materials, how to attain a purpose economically and without magic, and to develop a common sense which can come only from a more objective orientation to reality. In addition, of course, the classroom, as the other areas of the child's living and working at

Linden Hill, provides an experience in learning to accept group needs and participate as a member of the group, in learning how to share an adult, how to listen and how to communicate.

One part of our program represents a more specialized and planned effort to utilize group situations in the treatment of our children. This is our clinical group work program, in which our children meet in small groups of four to six members once or twice a week for an hour and a half under trained leaders. Every student belongs to at least one such group and most are in two or more.

In designing these groups three major criteria are used. One set of groups is based on our clinical knowledge of the individual children. Another is based on our children's own choice of companions. The third is based on the children's interest in particular activities. In these small groups, all of which are voluntary, even more than in the living situation, where the structure of routine plays so important a part, we have fluidity and spontaneity of expression. The group, however, serves as a framework and a medium through which to stimulate the children toward interrelatedness. The skills of the group leader and his understanding of the child's total personality are utilized in the recognition and development of movement toward increased socialization. In this sense the clinical group work program serves as a sort of laboratory for the use of group experience in our total program.

In addition to its aim of helping our children develop improved relationships, the group work program provides each child with opportunities to evaluate objectively himself and others, to try out and practice newly achieved attitudes, habits and skills in this protected and limited setting. Finally, it aims at enabling each child, through the development of new knowledge and skills as well as the perfection of old ones, to achieve recognition, status, a feeling of accomplishment and sense of worth. In most of our groups, regardless of how they are set up, the group members at the beginning are basically so unrelated that the only thing keeping them in the same place at the same time is the relationship with the leader. The leader works toward stimulating interaction, exploring with the youngsters and interpreting the difficulties they experience as they get closer to one another in the group.

We have found that, while on the surface it may appear as if some of our youngsters have good relationships with each other, further examination reveals that this is a pseudo relatedness and that any intensive and protracted experience in which inter-relatedness is taxed results in a breaking down of the façade. Essentially these youngsters are merely acting as if they were relating. The "as if" quality they establish is a strong component of their defenses and often gives the impression to the casual observer that they are much healthier than in reality they are.

Activities in our group work program assume unique characteristics. Food, for example, plays an extremely important role and is frequently the only basis around which some of our students can interact. Their basic infantilism is never clearer than when one observes the intense preoccupation they have with food and their almost animalistic approach to activities involving securing, preparing and consuming food. Almost all of our groups make continual and consistent use of food to entice, bind and maintain the group.

Tommy, with his inability to bear even brief closeness with other children, had great difficulty in even tentatively entering a group. For a long time he literally circled group activities, walking around and around. When food was served, he would dart in, grab his handful, gulp it down and then return to his encircling movements. This is a boy who avidly memorizes train schedules, keeps tabs on the mileage of staff members' cars, confronts each person when there is any deviation from schedule. He has a preoccupation with knowing what is going on in meetings, which seems partly to explain his need to encircle the group rather than leave it entirely. We took advantage of his compulsiveness and curiosity by giving him the responsibility of keeping the minutes of certain groups, and although his relatedness is still minimal, he has participated in this way in several groups and interaction with others is occurring.

At the beginning in our group work program, as in the living situation and in the classroom, our design had to be shaped around the extreme incapacities of our children. There is a constant need for re-evaluation of our program and the infusion of new ideas, not only because of the children's changing interests, but as a result of the changes that occur as they mature and develop. What we have learned up to now in our group work program is how the adults' awareness of and utilization of our children's patterns of reaction and interaction can serve to guide them toward greater interrelatedness and help bridge the gap between isolation and socialization. Similarly, in our school program we have been developing approaches whereby the adult can serve as a medium through which our children can learn to deal objectively with reality. In our living program we are attempting to accomplish both of these things, through an adaptation of the methods more easily discernible in the more formalized school and group work programs.

Research we see as a means of examining and evaluating our program to help point the direction of our movement. A continuous evaluation of our intake policy, the attempt to measure the change or lack of change in our children, the close examination of their behavior in more or less structured situations and analysis of their communication, are some of the ways in which we attempt to secure information that will help us to continue designing our program. A study of staff reactions to the children and to one another will, we hope, help us to make more effective the part which we as individuals and as a group play in making the setting therapeutic. Among our long-range research interests is the attempt to evaluate the relationship between what we find in our terribly disturbed children and the variegated phenomena of normal adolescence.

As in all treatment, and particularly in residential treatment, the central problem at Linden Hill is to maintain a successful balance between extremes, the individual and the group, the inner needs and the reality demands, the ego and the id, and to work toward a synthesis. With our children, for whom these gaps are so wide, our approach at Linden Hill may be summarized in these terms: We attempt to provide a flexible, tolerant and gentle milieu in which a great amount of satisfaction of basic needs is possible. At the same time we attempt, through adult example and guidance, through the gradual demands which we make of our children, and through the structure which we try to develop for them, to move them toward greater acceptance of reality demands and of the needs of socialization. Through education in living and through guided interaction, we attempt to lead them to a higher level of integration both within themselves and with social reality. These are the problems which are presented to our staff from minute to minute in one form or another. In the morning they may feel that they are running a very pleasant boarding school, and in the afternoon that they are supervising a hospital ward of psychotic patients. Each day the ward must be re-formed into a school and we must hope that our children are learning with us how better and more effectively to form order out of chaos.

THE NURSERY GROUP EXPERIENCE

6 ## AS PART OF A DIAGNOSTIC STUDY

OF A PRESCHOOL CHILD

Peter B. Neubauer, M.D., Augusta Alpert, Ph.D.,
and *Barbara Bank*

I

IN THIS PAPER we should like to present an extension of our diagnostic study process with preschool children and their families. This process reflects a number of specific features in our clinical work with the prelatency child. The program of the Child Development Center focuses on the treatment and study of preschool children with character disturbances, forerunners of neurotic symptom formation and other disturbances in development. Our interest therefore excludes the mentally deficient, organically disturbed and psychotic child.

Our families apply to us through our outpatient department, which fulfills two functions: diagnostic evaluation of the child and family; and the formulation of a treatment plan which may lead to referral, treatment in the outpatient department, or acceptance into the inpatient program. The latter consists of a day nursery with which is associated an intensive psychotherapeutic service.

Differences between the prelatency and the latency child affecting diagnostic study.—During the prelatency period, psychic structure—that is, superego, ego, and id—is in its developing stage. The superego is in the process of being formed. The prelatency child, therefore, will show more fluid defense mechanisms; will within one interview produce various material from different phases of development; will be able to regress to different levels—all in a very short period of time. In latency, however, the problem will be more defined, since the psychic structure will be more developed.

The structural difference also implies a dynamic difference, expressed in the transference relationship. In prelatency, the therapist will become, in varying degrees, part of the conflict. The transference neurosis is not developed. The therapist might be perceived as another doctor who is feared, which may lead to total inhibition of material and clinging to mother, until this fantasy can be corrected. The impact of external reality on fantasy will take a much longer time, since reality testing, too, is in the process of development, and the difference between fantasy and reality is still dim. The older child is more able to differentiate various situations from each other. These considerations will affect our diagnostic study.

In addition, in prelatency, it is more difficult to differentiate problems from pathology. While we expect that each phase of development has its own normal degree of problems and that problem solving is essential for normal development, we are faced with the question of diagnosing and assessing whether such problems are not already signs of disturbances. It is important to emphasize this, since we frequently speak too easily about "problems," without separating normal from pathological problems. It may be suggested to use the term "problem" for the normal encounters in solving the contradiction between instinctual demands and the environment, and the term "conflict" for those which express pathology.

It is not too difficult to diagnose the more serious disturbances, particularly where we find organic components—that is, the mentally defective, organically disturbed and schizophrenic child. Since the Center is interested in developmental disturbances, it is easy to see that the younger the child, the more difficult it will be to make a correct diagnosis.

The conventional tools in the study of children.—The common tools of our clinical study are the interview of child and parents, the medical examination and the psychological test.

From these, we obtain the somatic condition, the expression of emotional symptoms, the present modes of functioning and its history. These tools have to be retested for their usefulness for the preschool child.

The clinical worker will be very careful about the kind of environment he creates in the interview, and he has learned to behave in a way which will maintain the therapeutic climate; that is, he will be careful in the choice of stimulation he presents to the child. The observation of the child in this one-to-one relationship provides very important data, but does not permit us to judge with sufficient conviction the child's reaction to stimulations other than those set up by the worker in his play room. The child's behavior, therefore, will be selective. We are usually insufficiently aware of this aspect of our interview situation, particularly for diagnostic purposes.

At times, the interview situation may not invite the expression of the child's central conflict; it may even be such that it eliminates the possibility for the expression of the child's true problems and symptoms. A child, for example, may show his faulty relationship with adults by his severe sibling rivalry. In an interview, alone with one adult, this may not come to the fore. Usually, a careful history helps us to fill this gap; we can ask how the child reacted to outside experiences and correlate this with our experiences here. But this is difficult to do with a three-year-old, for instance, who has never had an experience which will provide such a history. The child's reaction to the experience of the nursery school may be very different from his social experience within the family. We therefore may not obtain the answers to our questions about the degree of education the child is able to absorb and his capacity for social adjustment in an educational setting. But it is just these factors which play an important part in the growth and development of the child. It will therefore be difficult to plan his readiness for nursery school participation, either outside or within the Center. In addition, we cannot determine the degree to which his behavior in the educational situation reflects his problems or his ability to cope with conflicts within the familial scene.

One is forced to judge the child's total personality much more carefully, in order to be able to make predictions about his health or pathology. Unfortunately, our field is not yet sufficiently developed to give us understanding of individual life situations and patterns of development with enough certainty to make such predictions. Our feeling of discomfort about a position which is based on such predictions led us to experiment with the usefulness of a nursery group as a diagnostic tool.

The preliminary diagnostic study brings its formulations to the nursery school. We ask the teacher to make specific observations which will either confirm the clinical material obtained or add different material, which may shift the initial interpretation of the history as given or expand it into areas as yet unknown. It is, so to speak, a "prescription" which is given to the teacher, in order to outline the kind of program which will be useful for diagnostic purposes. We add, thereby, new but controlled environmental stimulation to the child, in order to judge his reactions to it.

In addition to the study of the individual child, the outpatient nursery group (as distinguished from our inpatient therapeutic day nursery) affords us an additional important opportunity, namely, to study the parents in such a situation. The mother, too, may be confronted with a new experience: to let others plan for her child for a substantial part of the day. She may anticipate difficulties or pleasure in this new step, but she too will not be able to give us the history which may confirm either reaction. Here we can see her responding to the child's movement to a new step—we see her anxieties if she is afraid to lose the child, or her overreadiness if she wants us to relieve her of her own parental responsibilities.

Another important point is the possibility for a mother to observe the teacher's techniques of educating her child. This will allow us to see new and different aspects of the mother's personality, which cannot be observed in the regular interview situation, namely, her readiness to imitate and to understand the educational guidance of her child by others. This permits us to study the mother's capacity to learn. The nursery experience, therefore, becomes a tool not only for the study of the child, but also of that part of the family dynamics related to the mother-child interaction, and of the mother's and child's reactions to the teacher.

We would like to stress this point. The therapeutic relationship usually invites transference experiences, rather than a more active participation of nonconflicted ego functions. The teacher demonstrates what one can do with the child in different situations, in accordance with her judgment of the child's capacity. This is tested in reality and will therefore achieve a particular meaning to those parents who are able to see it. All those who have observed teachers in their everyday work will know how specific the reaction is to such a reality situation.

One may raise the question whether such an educational group is necessary for diagnostic studies; whether one cannot make sufficiently clear deduction as to the child's and parent's behavior from our conventional study. It is our impression that such an educational experience provides us with additional diagnostic information. The following presentation should show its advantages.

II

Observation of a child's functioning in a group of peers is an important part of diagnosis. In cases where children are already enrolled in a nursery group outside the Center, the team member assigned to the study observes the child in that setting. However, this does not give us an opportunity to observe interaction between parent and child, or between siblings, so that in some cases, even those children currently enrolled in nursery school will be invited to our outpatient nursery. We see this group not as a purely educational experience, but as a "prescription" nursery, where information gained by members of the team can be checked, confirmed, contradicted or supplemented by other team members, namely, teachers and research workers. We use educational materials and techniques as tools of diagnosis. The worker summarizes her impressions and makes recommendations which serve to suggest points of approach or special areas of observation.

We have from four to seven children in the group at a time. Questions as to grouping by age or symptomatology will not be discussed here; we have found that such a factor as age range, for instance, does not have the same meaning for this fluctuating group as it would for a purely educational group. We do not consider that for all children studied diagnostically a group experience is advisable, but in 1954-55 we saw fifty-one individual children in the outpatient nursery group. One child attended the group eleven times, but the average attendance is closer to four or five sessions. By the time the child comes to the outpatient group for the first time (and "the group" is a fluctuating one in composition), he has been in the Center building at least once before for an individual interview with the worker.

We have had the opportunity to observe siblings as they play together; in many cases we have had children who are enrolled in our inpatient nursery present when a younger sister or brother attended. The group meets in one of the Center nursery rooms after our school hours, from 2:00 to 3:30, one afternoon a week. The adults who serve as teachers are the educational director of the Center's regular nursery, chief psychiatric social worker and one of the Center nursery teachers. In addition, the worker who has been seeing the parents and who has seen the child previously is present.

The room is equipped for many activities: use of paints, clay, water, collage materials, dramatic, doll and block play, construction, manipulative activities, puzzles, games, etc. There is a period of free time, followed by a snack time at which we ask the children to sit down to milk, sandwiches and cookies. When the weather is good, we have used the roof play area where we have an opportunity to observe more of the large motor abilities of the children. We have attempted to provide opportunities for group experience, both for small groups within the free play period, centered around one of the activities such as collage, water play, block-building, etc., as well as an activity planned for the total group, such as the snack time, music, story or a game. We have been impressed by the ability of some of the children to find ways and means of making the environment more familiar: for one little girl, watering the plants in the room was a way of re-establishing familiarity; to another, a particular toy or material was primary in importance. Not to mention, of course, those who respond to a familiar adult face! Though the group of children is not constant, and the lack of complete familiarity inhibits relationships to a great extent, some children have remembered the names of children present at previous sessions and have looked for them immediately.

Rosalind J. came to us in January, at the age of three years and three months. A brother was born when Rosalind was two years and eight months. Mr. and Mrs. J. seemed an intelligent, cooperative couple, devoted to Rosalind and proud of her. The problems they presented were Rosalind's fears, extreme timidity, particularly with adults, and inability to deal with aggressive children. She was too docile, too submissive, friendly with family and excessively shy with strangers and fearful of new situations. The worker described Rosalind as "attractive, bright, competent." She reported that Rosalind related to her quickly and allowed her mother to leave the room for a while. Rosalind displayed skill in her use of materials, and excellent ability to verbalize. Some overmeticulousness was noticed. The recommendation was made that we see Rosalind in our outpatient nursery group for observation in the following areas: "Rosalind's ability to relate to other children and to a group, interaction between mother and child, Rosalind's ability to use equipment and plastic materials, her motor coordination, especially her gait." It was further noted that Rosalind might be a possibility for our nursery next year.

Rosalind attended the group for four consecutive sessions in January. In the first session we noted that she "appeared somewhat timid and not interested in other children, except for looking at them. She showed some interest in the toys and equipment around the sink and the kitchen corner. Her approach in general, however, was cautious. We observed that Rosalind used running in preference to walking. The running movements were below the level we would expect from a three-year-old, and she seemed uncertain on her feet." In the second session, Rosalind quickly expressed pleasure at recognizing pieces of equipment with which she had played the previous week. At certain moments during the afternoon, she seemed determined to enjoy herself in her own way. If one of the teachers or her mother tried to make an activity or material more appealing to her, she quietly, but firmly, did it her own way. No "excessive shyness" was noted, but rather a "cautious reserve." During this visit she again had very little contact with other children, but she continued to look around at them and at the adults. She had difficulty becoming absorbed in something which interested her, looking into many boxes and trying to do many things with puzzles, peg boards, blocks, crayons and clay. Her fine motor coordination was good, but her activities were continuously interrupted, partly because of her watchfulness of others. Even while absorbed in drawing, she watched the children and adults. She did not initiate contact with other children during these first two sessions, nor did she actively seek contact with the teachers. She could accept suggestions from the adults if they were related to an activity in which she was interested; when she was uninterested, she did not express this negatively, but sat and did nothing. She was able to communicate some experiences to teachers. During the first two visits, Rosalind sought her mother's attention and help for certain things such as dressing dolls, ran to her frequently and sought her out constantly with her eyes.

By the third visit, Rosalind sought the teacher's attention and help for dressing dolls. It seemed to us that she was able to do this herself, but wanted adult support and was at this point able to seek it from one of the teachers. By this time she showed interest in the surroundings of the nursery which had become familiar to her. She began to take an interest in a slightly older little girl, Janet, who was also attending the group for the third time. During this session, Rosalind was able to let her mother leave the room to sit in an adjoining office. This also was one of the first times Janet had been able to move some distance from *her* mother and when Rosalind noticed Janet's looking around anxiously, she put her hand on Janet's, and with some impatience assured her that her mother was there, saying, "Don't you see!" Rosalind was able to let her mother leave briefly, but still could not sustain an activity with another child, or with a group. It was obvious that Rosalind was overtired at moments, which seemed to be due to the fact that attendance in the group meant missing her normal afternoon nap.

On her fourth and final visit, Rosalind was very sleepy, but showed distinct signs of pleasure when meeting another little girl, Lois, who had also attended previous sessions. She used paints (although she rejected paste). She showed an interest in the story which was read by a teacher. When her view of the storybook was deliberately blocked by an aggressive little boy she was able to move herself into a position where she could see.

It was clear by her verbal and physical overtures that two children, Janet and Lois, had come into her focus of attention. This was supplemented by the mother's reports to the caseworker (whom she was seeing on a regular basis) that Rosalind spoke frequently at home of the group, mentioned the children by name, and had approached the children she knew when she met them on the street after the sessions.

Our impression of the interaction between Rosalind and her mother during the group sessions was that Mrs. J. at first seemed too anxious to step in and made many suggestions to supplement those of the teachers. Rosalind, in turn, frequently ran to her mother to show her something or to ask her permission to do something. Rosalind was dressed immaculately, and we thought that not only was she afraid to do things, but that Mrs. J. was afraid to let her. As Mrs. J.'s tension decreased, Rosalind was freer to move away from her toward the group.

During the first session when Mrs. J. left the room for several minutes, Rosalind did not ask for her, but occasionally said "Mommy" when utilizing the teacher's help. The experience of observing the group was an important one for Mrs. J. and she told the therapist she had been helped to "observe" Rosalind's behavior at home. Although she had of course known that Rosalind's slight orthopedic disability needed eventual correction, it was the experience of seeing her in a group of children which made Mrs. J. aware of the need to think about doing something about it soon. Rosalind's comfortable reaction to the adults did not confirm Mrs. J.'s feeling that Rosalind was excessively shy and fearful of all new people and situations. Her behavior in the group had not been that of an excessively clinging child, and this is something we could not have known as fully had we not seen Rosalind in the nursery setting. Discussion of Rosalind's fatigue, and fuller clarification of her sleeping difficulties, led Mrs. J. to increased awareness of the source of difficulty in the mother-child relationship itself, and enabled her and her therapist to move more quickly to deeper discussion

of relevant material. Mrs. J. saw that the teachers did not anticipate Rosalind's every need and did not offer help prematurely.
She began to see her own overidentification with her child.

The description of Rosalind's behavior given by her mother
was not borne out by what we observed in the outpatient nursery. We observed that anxiety prevented her from interacting
with other children; and her behavior with them resembled that
of a much younger child. Her use of materials was age-adequate,
but we saw evidences of overmeticulousness in her concern over
clothes and her avoidance of paste. With the teachers in the
group, as with the therapist she saw alone, Rosalind seemed
more independent and assured. In the first three group visits,
Rosalind sought out her mother by running to her or looking
for her, but this could be seen in terms of the mother's need
and Rosalind was able to have her mother leave the room
during the fourth session.

At a conference in February, the Center staff decided to admit
the J. family into our program. Rosalind is being introduced to
our youngest nursery group two mornings a week. Although she
has different teachers and is in a different room from that used
by the outpatient nursery group, she has been able to "carry
over" this first group experience and is reacting comfortably,
though, of course, cautiously, to the new situation. Her mother
is still there, but from her teacher's positive reports we do not
believe separation will present an acute problem.

III

Diagnostic evaluation, as seen at the Child Development
Center, is a complex and continuous process. The evaluation of
the child is inseparable from that of the parents, particularly
the mother. The total diagnostic process passes through four
stages:

(1) The parents' statement of the problem.
(2) History taking. This period overlaps period 3, which in
    turn guides the interviewer as to further scrutiny of
    parents' reports.

(3) Observation of the child in the outpatient department nursery.

(4) The integration and evaluation of the assembled data by the team of observers and therapists.

In the case of Rosalind, the problem as stated by the parents was that the child was extremely timid, docile, fearful and excessively clinging, especially to the mother. She was said to be excessively shy with strangers.

The history was obtained from the parents, who were bright, sensitive and cooperative. The reliability of the mother was somewhat questionable, however, in view of her overinvolvement with the child which at times led to questions as to whether her observations were accurate representations of Rosalind's behavior or whether they represented projections of her own feelings and impulses.

Rosalind was the product of an anxious pregnancy and a difficult birth. Her mother had had two previous pregnancies which had terminated in miscarriage; the third was almost as unsatisfactory, since she had to take pills throughout to forestall another threatened abortion. She felt that Rosalind was "manufactured, not born," and was the end result of two previous failures, rather than a child in her own right. She was born prematurely after four days of false labor and fourteen hours of extremely difficult true labor. High forceps had to be used, and Rosalind was very frail at birth.

Early feeding was difficult and laborious, since Rosalind showed little eagerness for the bottle, falling asleep readily and requiring up to one and a half hours to complete a feeding. She rarely seemed hungry. She was weaned sensitively and easily at sixteen to eighteen months. Feeding was complicated by the early appearance of allergies, which first manifested themselves at three months with a severe facial eczema. Dietary manipulation resulted in elimination of the symptom at six months, and it has not recurred. At two, however, there was swelling of the face and eyes; a bland diet was again instituted. Currently she shows an extraordinarily acute contact sensitivity to certain foods, such as smoked fish, reacting with hives, swellings, etc. Small doses of benadryl relieve the symptoms promptly.

Toilet training was handled flexibly, and Rosalind responded readily; indeed, there are suggestions of overcompliance. Daytime training began at fourteen months and was completed by two for both bowels and bladder; night training occurred abruptly at two and a half, when Rosalind was given a new bed and told she had to be dry. She was.

Rosalind had always put things in her mouth. She was a fairly severe thumb-sucker in infancy and still sucks her thumb to fall asleep. In her crib she had sucked the corner of the pad, but gave this up immediately on the mother's suggestion when moved to her new bed. However, she still enjoys sucking on toys, her bathrobe, etc. Since she has partially renounced thumb-sucking she has been noted occasionally to lick her finger and rub it on her cheek.

Speech developed early, much to the parents' joy. She began using words at eight months and spoke sentences by one year. Her motor development was, however, slower; she did not walk until fifteen to sixteen months.

Sleep was an area of considerable difficulty for Rosalind. During her second year she began waking frequently, demanding attention from her parents. The real sleeping problems began, though, at three years and one month, two months before Rosalind came to the Center. Disturbed by the story of Little Red Riding Hood, she began waking regularly, asking for her mother, wanting the door open and wishing reassurance of her mother's proximity. This situation has improved markedly since Rosalind has been at the Center, so that now the parents are surprised by a bad night. Rosalind still reports occasional fearsome dreams about animals. Rosalind's mother, incidentally, suffers from insomnia.

The principal complaint of shyness and fear of strangers dates from the age of six months, when Rosalind showed fear of the doctor around her third immunization injection. Until two and a half, her fear seemed to revolve around men, but then extended to women. She was always extremely sensitive to any kind of disturbing stimulus; there seemed to be heightened reaction to noise from as early as three months. She is extremely sensitive to any slight or harshness from adults.

There has been an unusual degree of fastidiousness from very early in life. As an infant Rosalind disliked the feel of grass or carpet under her, and crawled in an odd way to avoid contact with such surfaces. (While still in the baby carriage she would hold her hands in the air to avoid touching things.) She has always shown some fear of sand and a dislike of the feel of it on her hands, and manifests an acute distaste for anything slimy. Rosalind's way of dealing with new situations is to avoid looking at them; once she has had an experience she will eagerly anticipate re-experiencing it.

Observation of the child in the outpatient department nursery confirmed, modified and expanded the parents' description of her. She behaved like an anxious child who had to maintain a

looking-seeking contact with the mother. For several days looking was her only contact with other children and their activities.
So imperative was this looking that it interrupted every activity
she undertook. Thus her anxiety not only prevented her from
free contact with people and things, but it also interrupted contacts, making for marked discontinuity.

Rosalind's relations with other children in the group reflected
her problem. Her first relationship was with Janet, another
anxious, passive child. Actually, their contact might better be
called "resonance" than "relationship." She picked up Janet's
anxiety regarding her mother, and defended herself against her
own separation anxiety by impatiently reassuring Janet that her
mother was there ("Don't you see!"). When crowded out of a
reading group she did not protest, but instead accommodated
herself to the barrier imposed on her by a boy and moved away.

It was felt by the observers in the nursery that Rosalind's
docility had the quality of passive resistance; this seemed to be
born out by the unfolding history.

Integration of this history with the actual observations of the
child yielded a comprehensive view of the problem. Rosalind's
passivity was seen as the interaction between a constitutional
make-up[1] and a developmental response to the world around
her. Her early inactivity and markedly slowed feeding pattern
were reflected in the nursery, where it took her fifteen minutes
to eat a piece of toast. Her extreme docility and easy renuncia-
tion of instinctual gratification were exemplified in the toilet
training and weaning experiences. Her easy fatigability was
seen as another indication of a constitutional passivity and lack
of drive. It seemed generally easier for Rosalind to withdraw
from any challenge than to engage herself in it. This appeared
to be one determinant of her avoidance of new situations and
new people, and her inability to defend herself.

Another factor that emerged from the integration was Rosa-

[1] A. Alpert, P. Neubauer and A. Weil, Unusual Variations in Drive
Endowment. *The Psychoanalytic Study of the Child, 11.* New York: International Universities Press, 1956.

lind's tendency toward early somatization, as seen in her eczema and allergies. Related to this in the current picture were her extreme fastidiousness, with avoidance of tactile stimulation, and her preference for looking rather than touching or doing. Here, of course, there is a marked admixture of other elements; in the case of the fastidiousness, a considerable role must be allotted to the mother's own overmeticulousness, while in the case of her preference for looking, the above-mentioned passivity plus a hypercathexis of looking plays a prominent part.

The marked accentuation and prolongation of Rosalind's "anxiety of the stranger" was the outstanding presenting feature. Normally seen at about eight months, "anxiety of the stranger" reflects the infant's growing awareness of the distinction between his mother and other adults and the fear of loss of the mother which the presence of another adult suggests. In Rosalind, partly in response to the traumatic experience with the doctor, but especially because of the above-mentioned exaggerated sensitivity to any disturbing stimulus and the symbiotic tie with the mother, this phenomenon was heightened in intensity and persisted until the time of referral to the Center.

In diagnostic terms, the relationship between Rosalind and her parents could best be described as a "resonant symbiosis," in which all three contributed to a three-way projection system. The mother's contribution centered around her anxiety about her own health and her status as a carrier of a hereditary blood disease, together with her two previous unsuccessful pregnancies and her insomnia. She showed an extremely strong identification with Rosalind, expressed in her conviction that she feels what the child feels and the child feels what she feels. It is this symbiosis that makes observation of the child, with and without the mother's presence, in an atmosphere uncharged with anxiety, essential for the diagnostic process. In addition, the mother manifested considerable guilt about her exploitation of Rosalind's docility.

Rosalind's contribution to this "resonant symbiosis" was her constitutional inactivity, her anxious dependency, the continuation far beyond the normal infantile period of her concentrated looking at and for the mother. The father's contribution was his anxious fear that something would happen to the child when he was absent from home. He preferred to minimize the problem, relating Rosalind's timidity to the parents' shyness and hoped that she would "outgrow it all."

Diagnosis, of course, carries with it a tacit or implicit prognosis. In this situation, prediction depends on certain variables in the total complex. First, the question of the parents' susceptibility to therapeutic influence can be answered fairly positively. They are both bright, devoted, cooperative people who show every indication of being accessible. The child also indicates some amenability to neutralization of the "resonant symbiosis" in her behavior in the nursery group. The fact of her beginning relationship with Janet, together with her development of defenses against her separation anxiety, points in this direction. Further, her beginning movement toward a more active role in the group suggests some modifiability of her basic passivity, at least in an environment which encourages and stimulates such activity. These are favorable signs. Rosalind's ability to overcome her anxiety away from the contagious anxiety of the mother must be further studied, as must her ability to overcome her overfastidiousness. Though the latest report from the regular nursery indicated that Rosalind had finally permitted herself to touch clay, her reluctance to touch and her reliance on looking may significantly interfere with the capacity for sublimation.

It can be seen, then, that diagnosis of the preschool child is a continuing process. It does not end with the play interview, or the developmental history. It must be a product of a process of direct observation and integration of a variety of sources of information, and will generally continue well beyond the formal "diagnostic" phase into the period of therapeutic management. Careful observation is essential to discriminate what is pathology from what is an inevitable or phase-appropriate developmental problem. The multifaceted program of the Child Development Center is designed to meet this challenge.

PART III

THE PROBLEM OF THE SEVERELY DISTURBED CHILD

THE JEWISH BOARD of Guardians, like most other child guidance agencies, has become increasingly interested in and concerned with the problem of the atypical or schizophrenic child. This interest has been reflected in the clinical and research activities of the agency, and in its publications. The paper by Dr. Nagelberg et al. is the outgrowth of a project in the treatment of the "borderline" child which was carried on at the Bronx office of the Madeleine Borg Child Guidance Institute, under the direction of Dr. Hyman Spotnitz.

The consideration by Dr. Goldfarb et al. of a special type of family interaction pattern in the severely disturbed child, while representing some of the work being done at the Henry Ittleson Center for Child Research, also points up JBG's concern for the role of the total family unit in the pathological and therapeutic processes.

The final paper, a report of a series of discussions of a single atypical child, demonstrates the operation and the value of the agency's multidisciplinary approach to the understanding of clinical problems.

THE ATTEMPT AT HEALTHY

7 INSULATION IN THE

WITHDRAWN CHILD

Leo Nagelberg, Ph.D., Hyman Spotnitz, M.D., Med.Sc.D., and *Yonata Feldman*

IN A PREVIOUS report, two of the writers (Nagelberg and Spotnitz, 1952) described some material from a group of schizophrenic children and outlined desirable initial steps in the treatment of them. The purpose of the treatment was to cope with the excessive impulsivity which, it appeared, made necessary the development of the schizophrenic syndrome in the children described. The present report deals with one aspect of the schizophrenic syndrome—namely, the mechanism of emotional withdrawal which seems to be necessary for some children in order to insulate themselves from the strong pressures of the environment or, specifically, from the excessive emotional impact of their parents.

Freud (1922) suggested the problem when he wrote: "For the living organism, protection against stimuli is almost a more important task than the reception of stimuli; the protective barrier is equipped with its own store of energy and must above all endeavor to protect the special forms of energy transformations going on within itself from the equalizing and therefore destructive influence of the enormous energies at work in the outer world."

The child needs to be protected against any overwhelming stimulation. As mentioned by Bergman and Escalona (1949), insufficiency of the stimulus barrier may lead to the formation of a premature ego organization which may dispose a child to the development of a psychosis.

The relatively healthy child has learned through parental understanding, care and protection to differentiate himself from his parents. If the parent is too stimulating or inadequate to prevent overstimulation, the child finds in his parent insufficient protection, his protective barrier is inadequate, and his health and survival are threatened. Because in the relatively unhealthy child, parental care, understanding and protection are lacking, the tendency of the child may be to withdraw emotionally in order to supply by a substitutive process the necessary insulation.

The therapeutic sessions to be briefly described were conducted (by L.N.) with the idea in mind that possibly the children were using emotional withdrawal as a method of achieving adequate insulation. The therapist therefore kept, whenever possible, the emotional impact of his own personality at a minimum and maintained as much emotional reserve as possible.

We are presenting case material of three children treated at the Madeleine Borg Child Guidance Institute of the Jewish Board of Guardians. The case reports are not intended to give complete case histories. We wish to show through the statements of the children what withdrawal meant to them and what purpose it served.

Case 1

Samuel, ten, was withdrawn. He had few friends. He refused to speak out loud in class. He would not leave the house without his mother. He was described by his mother as abnormally modest, terrified of his mother's seeing him naked. He never smiled or laughed out loud. He mumbled when he spoke, his facial expression was extremely rigid and impassive, he often ate alone in his room, and he would not permit anyone to sing in the house. He would not receive gifts or show any enjoyment when things were handed to him. He had an I.Q. of 152.

Samuel was the oldest of three children. The two younger ones were girls. The parents' marriage was not a happy one and the parents separated several times before they finally obtained a divorce when Samuel was five-and-one-half. He was not wanted by his father. His birth was a difficult one and the mother was in labor forty-eight hours. Low forceps were used. Samuel was breast-fed only for three weeks. From the age of three-and-one-half to nine months, he cried constantly because of insufficient food. From the day he was born, his stool was caught in Kleenex. He was never permitted to soil. At nineteen months, he had his tonsils removed. At twenty months, the child had a tantrum and his father slapped his face until Samuel was exhausted. At the age of two, he had a severe jaw tumor which required surgical treatment. As a result of this, many of his teeth had decayed. At three-and-one-half years of age, when he annoyed his mother, she pushed him and he fell on a lawn mower and sustained an injury which permanently crippled his thumb.

When the therapist saw Samuel for the first time, his eyes were alert but his facial expression was rigid. He refused to sit down and *kept at a distance* from the therapist. He looked at the objects in the room but did not touch them. He asked the therapist what his job was—had he read the book *Problems by Ripley?* He told the therapist that the problems given by Ripley often may take "a million years to solve." He himself was interested in higher mathematics, in very complicated problems. It was as if Samuel himself told the therapist how complicated his difficulties were and how long it would take to help him.

This idea was confirmed in the second interview when Samuel brought the therapist a kaleidoscope and again showed him "complicated designs." He told how he looked into freight cars, threw stones at hogs and bulls, and frightened animals. The bull made a noise like the atomic bomb. He suggested to the therapist that he read the *Book of Knowledge* which "gives you all the answers." Did the therapist know why old people die? At the end of this interview, he told the therapist, "You don't seem to understand me. Your language is different." One wonders whether Samuel had an inkling that he spoke in the language of symbols; only by understanding this language could one reach him.

In the third interview, Samuel brought in binoculars. The therapist was to look into other people's windows and solve puzzles. In this interview, Samuel went one step further. He told the therapist to read a certain book "which will teach you to become a detective." This gave a hint that the things which were so dangerous to look at have a criminal flavor. Samuel further promised to bring the therapist a book "full of interesting facts"; namely, it showed how a man could remain in ice for 1000 years and he would come to life again; also the ice (apparently freezing of emotions) could be used against cancer.

In the fourth interview, Samuel introduced a science magazine to show the therapist an article where healing was done through hypnosis. He showed him the picture of a sea mask; with these sea masks, one could swim under water for a long time. This was followed by Samuel's bringing the therapist a book on "personal magnetism" and another one on "how to read people's minds."

In all these interviews, Samuel suggested the insulating aspects of his withdrawal: one must protect oneself from danger, must freeze oneself, must preserve oneself in ice and not come to life prematurely, must hide under water. Convinced that the therapist remained at a distance and did nothing "to throw stones and to infuriate the hogs and bulls," i.e., refrained from stimulating his aggression, Samuel felt enough at ease to throw some light on the nature of the danger from these "animals" from which he must insulate himself or withdraw.

In the sixth interview, he built a tower and made a little ball. He rolled the ball toward the tower, and while he did this, he held his hand over his mouth. He expected the ball to make the tower collapse, and when the ball came close to the tower, he jumped back. In this interview, Samuel for the first time moved freely around the room and explored the objects. It should be noted that around this time, the mother phoned to say that Samuel had shown improvement in behavior. He now went to the park and played with other children. In the interviews, Samuel discovered as if for the first time the therapist as a person. He noticed his suit and said, "Can't we talk?" He bored a hole in clay, rolled another piece and tried to put it in the hole. At the same time, he told the therapist of animal movies which he said were taken at the risk of life of the people who took the picture.

This was followed by interviews where Samuel could display aggression directly. He brought guns, he ordered 100 firecrackers. He said he liked the smell, he liked the noise. One could also make a "booby trap" with fireworks. He added that perhaps this trap would be too small to kill a person. He told that he once killed a caterpillar. The smell of firecrackers reminded him of the smell of camels. He made a fire in the therapist's room. His aggressive activity gained momentum from interview to interview. This brought forth memories—a whirlwind he saw on his grandfather's farm. "If it hits you, it will throw you right into the air!" All during these aggressive reports, Samuel held his hands over his mouth as if trying to prevent the escape of his real wishes and drives through the medium of the word, as though he were a primitive who believed that there was magic in the word. When a thought was put into words, the deed was as if accomplished.

The therapist became somewhat impatient with Samuel's activities and asked him to tell him why he was coming and to tell about his present life and his past. Samuel said he did not wish to know why he was coming, and if the therapist would tell him what his problem was, he would never return again. Under the pressure of the therapist's desire to make the boy talk, his productions became confused. Samuel commented angrily that the therapist observed everything about him and that he was not able to move around. On various occasions, he would hide under the clothes rack or crawl under the desk.

When the therapist discontinued putting any questions to him, Samuel resumed his aggressive activities during the interviews. The therapist joined Samuel in whatever discussion he initiated. If he talked about maps, the therapist would talk about maps. If Samuel discussed cars, inventions, wars, the therapist would start talking about these topics. As the therapist went along with Samuel's resistiveness and, so to speak, took part in it, the boy's stiffness was replaced by more natural behavior for a boy of ten. He now spoke about his feelings toward the therapist. Positive feelings emerged. He did not like his mother to smoke but he did not mind if the therapist smoked. He would like the therapist to visit him in his home. Though he still told of "stink bombs one might suffocate from," he also asked the therapist to get him a volunteer who would be a Big Brother to him and take him out week ends.

At the end of the fortieth interview, the boy discussed plans to go to camp or visit his father, who lives in a different city. Though he still had compulsive symptoms, the immediate signs of his withdrawal had almost entirely disappeared.

The material presents evidence that Samuel was a traumatized child and that he feared injury to his ego. When he discovered that the therapist would not overstimulate or traumatize him, he began to feel free to express his own aggression, thoughts, feelings and impulses.

Case 2

Mary, age nine-and-one-half, was referred to the agency by her father because of her inability to adjust to other children. She preferred to stay at home and to engage in solitary activities. She read excessively and would cover 400 pages a day. Occasionally she seemed to be dazed, would sit by herself for long periods, and did not seem to be aware of what was going on. Until recently Mary used to clown in class, would refuse to follow the work that other children were doing, and would just walk out of the classroom. At times, she would pick up her skirt in class and put it over her head. Yet she was intellectually capable of doing the classwork. When she was seven, she rated an I.Q. of 194 on the Stanford-Binet. Two years later she was retested and rated only 124. Her inability to relate to children was observed when she was only five years of age. At that time, strong aggressive tendencies were also in evidence; she showed unusual sexual curiosity and used obscene language in a compulsive way. As time went on, her seclusiveness and remoteness from people became more pronounced.

Mary's father was a conscientious but unemotional sort of person.

Her mother was running from school to school and constantly interfered in the affairs of the child. She did not allow Mary to cross the
streets alone and dressed her although she was nine years old.

In her first contact with the therapist, Mary told him that she came to
talk about herself. Yet she spoke at great length about an imaginary
club consisting of ten girls and eleven boys. In her fantasy, this club
was ever-increasing in numbers and the proportion of males and
females was always kept intact. It was as if Mary formulated her problem to the therapist, her wish to take her place among a normal group
but which she could not realize in reality.

In the second interview, she enlarged upon why she had excluded
herself from the group and withdrawn. She told of the imaginary club
member, Jim, who shot Rose; he hit Martha with a drumstick and
crushed three animals and was excluded from the club.

In the third interview, Mary spilled water over her dress and cried
out, "My mother will think that I messed all over myself in the bathroom." For a nine-and-one-half-year-old child, it was rather unusual that
the act of spilling water should at once take her back to infantile wishes
and memories of strong maternal prohibitions. From then on, interview
after interview, she engaged in spilling ink, making ink blots, messing
around with ink. Guilt over messing expressed itself in a game of
hanging. "You hang the person who is wrong," she said. The therapist
asked her to tell him about her troubles. She replied, "I hope you will
not ask me questions about my troubles, because it almost makes me
cry." As the therapist slowed his pace, she told him that there was a
time when she played with real children. Having experienced the therapist's permission to play and mess with ink, she could make the next
step and told him, "I am curious about things but I am afraid to know
what I am curious about." It might be noted that whereas another child
would say that she was curious about things but was ashamed to talk
about her curiosity, Mary's statement was to the effect that "she herself
fears to know." This seemed to point to a much more primitive fear and
suggested that forbidden impulses were much closer to the surface.
Also greater energy had to be invested in repression and there was
greater anxiety about forbidden curiosity.

Then came the day in the twelfth interview when she came to see
the therapist in a new dress and told him that she was not going to
dirty herself. This was the first development of an ability to control
herself in the therapeutic setting. She made bizarre drawings and made
meaningless sounds and asked the therapist to repeat the sounds after
her. Mary said, "I can do it here and it is not crazy, but if I do it outside, people will call me crazy." A growing attachment to the therapist
manifested itself. She wished to stay longer with the therapist, to hold

his hand; she wanted him to lead her downstairs. As he permitted her to say "crazy" things, she felt he accepted her infantile wishes. They could come to light and be understood. She could invest her energies in more appropriate behavior. She could give up her "crazy" behavior.

In a subsequent interview, she produced an old memory. She told the therapist a story of a couple who stood before an infant's crib and the father said, "How cheap this crib is." Mary interpreted that the father did not mean the crib was cheap. He wanted to say that the infant was ugly. It was Mary herself who was ugly and crazy and afraid of what she was curious about, and again the therapist did not push away this "crazy person," but took her hand and led her down the stairs after the interview. Messing with ink was changed to more creative work with clay and joy at producing a real object, a Menorah, which she could have admired by her mother and brother. She made a gift for the therapist, a letterweight, something real and useful. She now began to tell the therapist about the real children in school. She attended a progressive school where children were permitted free expression of aggression. Mary could now understand that it was not that the children would attack her, but that she could not tolerate the sight of aggression. She cried; she begged to be allowed to change schools. In the meantime, she had acquired a girl friend. Mary changed her school and then her mother reported she was too busy with school activities and no longer had time to see the therapist.

The predominant theme which Mary presented in her interviews was that she could not tolerate aggressive behavior in other children. The acceptance of her demonstrated by the therapist gave her the feeling that she was worth while and had the right to assert herself and demand that she be placed in a school where children were less aggressive. Her ego had been threatened in the exposure to an extremely aggressive environment.

Case 3

Harry, referred at the age of thirteen, usually spoke in muffled tones in a low, monotonous voice. Whenever he spoke, he spoke haltingly and at times he was devoid of spontaneity. His mother complained that Harry had no friends, did not go into the street, and when he did, said hello to nobody. Although he was a brilliant student, he was losing interest in school and often would stay in bed all day long and miss school. When he was in bed, he frequently covered himself up with the sheet and listened to the radio. He preferred to be with his mother, and when he was out in the street, would stay close to a building. His mother said she had tried to encourage him to have friends, but he did not want any. When they came to the house at her invitation, he was annoyed. When friends would phone, he would tell his mother to tell them that he was not at home. At times, he hid in closets, bundled up in his blanket. He would lock his mother out of the room. Once when his mother undid the blanket, he was rolled up like a cocoon and was perspiring profusely and was quite exhausted.

Sometimes he told his mother that he loved her so much and then at other times he would tell her he had to kill her. He spat at her, took the belt off his pants and hit her, threatened to commit suicide. He would put a rope around his mother's neck, jump on her, and throw the pillow over her face, threatening to choke her.

The mother dated the difficulties to the death of her husband when Harry was five, after which she went to live with her own mother for two years. This two-year period with the maternal grandmother she felt caused the boy's present difficulties.

In the first interview, he expressed his unwillingness to come—there was nothing he had to say about himself. He summed up his life by saying, "I was born and am still living!" When he was told he did not have to come, he decided that he would come. The therapist did not put any pressure on him and Harry asked, "Why don't you persuade me to come?" No encouragement was given him to come and he volunteered, "I understand it's quite a privilege to come." The therapist refused to exert any pressure. Had it been applied, it might have resulted in Harry's withdrawal from the treatment situation. As he felt that no one pushed him to come, he was free to venture forward into the treatment situation.

The nonstimulating approach was continued. Harry continued to keep up his isolation by talking about his impersonal interest in science and planetary problems.

In the fourth interview, he was able to say that he felt better when he talked and when there was someone to listen to him. He maintained his suspicious attitude. In this interview he asked, "Would you consider it impolite if I would say that psychiatrists are not on the level?" He indicated that nobody was on the level and that he had to protect himself against a threatening environment.

In the fifth interview, he asked why the therapist smoked. Had he heard cigarettes contained nicotine? Nicotine was poisonous; it was dangerous and the therapist should show self-control. He asked, "How can you control others when you cannot control yourself?" Nicotine may go into the lungs and this may bring about cancer of the lungs. Again Harry demonstrated his fear that other people would not be able to control themselves, projecting his own fear that he was not able to keep himself in check. It was as if he thought that if people did not keep at a distance, an explosion would ensue. In the same interview, he told a story where a person was crippled but actually had benefited from his broken leg because people gave him gifts of money. Harry said, "It's better for people sometimes if they are sick." It was an advantage to be sick and not to participate.

In the sixth interview, he initiated a method which he was to keep up for some time. He asked what the thoughts of the therapist were about political questions. He explained that this was a method of keeping the therapist at a distance. Harry must avoid talking about himself or drawing attention to himself. On the surface, it seemed that he was showing an interest in the therapist, but actually he was not interested at all in the worker as a person but only attempting to keep him away.

In the seventh interview, Harry said he was impelled to talk about impersonal objects, hobbies, museums, stamp collection, in order to keep the therapist away. "However, I realize that you are not interested when I talk about impersonal things. I know because if I don't talk about my personal opinions, I will not be helped." Harry was now more ready to discuss personal matters.

In the next interview, Harry looked much better and showed more spontaneity. He was friendly, and although he still spoke in a muffled tone, there was some animation. He said he himself was surprised that he liked school now. He also had a friend who bred fish and his hobby now was to protect fish. "Female fish devour their own eggs, and when eggs are produced, one has to separate the eggs from the female fish."

In a subsequent interview, he spoke in more detail about his hobby of taking care of fish. He came back to the theme that big fish might kill little fish and he had to separate them. If they were too big, they would eat the small fish. Separation was necessary. A balance had to be maintained, too, to keep the tank clean. It suggested the idea that he had to continue his withdrawal and that it was necessary for him to maintain a balance. In the same interview, he went a step further and suggested the next problem, namely, that of his confusion about male and female identification. In this interview, he spoke about baseball games, the World Series, and then went back to the fish tank and told the therapist that he had bought a book on how to breed fish. He told the therapist how one can distinguish between female and male fish and then he said, "I hear little fish cannot be distinguished yet as to whether they are male or female, but in time I will be able to do so." In the next interview, he discussed different types of fish and made a drawing of a fish. There was danger for this fish because this type of fish could not stop by itself and would drop dead if it brushed against a rock.

In the fourteenth interview, Harry was able to discuss his mother. He said he had an argument with his mother because he did not go to school today. They had lots of arguments. He insulted his mother and then threw up his meal. He said, "If Mother only would not take me so seriously, but she won't. Mother wants me to go out but I like to read, practice the clarinet. My mother interrupts me and wants me to go on errands but I don't want to."

In the seventeenth interview, he said that he had decided that he would talk more openly to the therapist. Last week he cried and thought nobody loved him. "I often thought that I can only get satisfaction from myself; that is, I have to like myself because nobody likes me. No one really understands me; for this reason, I prefer to stay home and not go out."

In other interviews, he spoke more about his mother and he said, "I do homework much better when Mother leaves the house and *I work best if I'm separated.*" He brought out a number of critical remarks against his mother and then he looked at the therapist and said, "I feel you understand. You certainly know that I really love my mother even if I say that I don't love her. One part loves my mother and the other part does not."

In the nineteenth interview, Harry said that he had joined a club and he would like the therapist to give him some ideas on how to run this club. He thought the therapist could give him good ideas and that "you have the right psychology and I might use it for the club. It's important to use the right psychology. One teacher asked me to recite a poem. First I said no, but the teacher did not bother me and then I became interested and I was willing to recite the poem. If people are direct and tell me what to do, I will say no, but if they say I shouldn't do it, I'll do it." Harry again demonstrated his negative suggestibility, *his need to go contrary to all direction because he felt he must separate himself sufficiently from other people before he could participate on his own.*

Again he felt that the therapist used the right psychology. "You showed discretion, didn't show any interest but I continued to come. If you had said, 'Come,' I would have laughed to myself and said ha-ha, and surely I would not have come. Secondly, you showed the right psychology because you arranged it in such a way that you helped me to find a solution for myself. I think that you and I actually always have the same idea. A good psychologist is a person who makes the other person express what the psychologist thinks, and then the other person feels happy about it."

Several times he tried to get the opinion of the therapist, to test out whether the latter would intervene, but the therapist remained noncommittal. For instance, he wanted to know whether he should or should not talk with other boys, whether he should or should not fight with his mother; and regularly he would come back and say that the therapist had used the right psychology when he did not intervene.

More and more he became interested to know how the therapist put pieces together. He said, "I know you watch me and put pieces together, but how do you do it? I think you do it because you listen to me, watch me; you watch me even if I yawn. I would like to get from you complete instructions on how to put pieces together. I think I have to learn something from you, and this is how one goes about putting people together. These are the rules: First, listen. Second, don't rush to get all problems. Third, wait until the other person has something to offer too."

His drive to become a good psychologist became stronger. He said he was interested in becoming a psychologist himself. The therapist asked him, "Suppose you become a psychologist, what would you get out of that?" His reply was that he would no longer need to come. Evidently if he should become like the therapist, then the therapist would become superfluous. The need to become like the therapist had some positive aspects in that Harry wanted to identify himself with or incorporate "a good father." Still, one should not omit seeing that Harry also demonstrated his defensive technique which consisted of swallowing up the object—the therapist—who was dangerous. The therapist or the outside world was also a menace to him against which he could only defend himself by becoming like the object. On the surface this attitude showed compliance, interest, a need to please, flattery; but these were also defensive devices to get the worker out of the way. Harry continued to say that he wanted to read psychology books so he would be able to handle people. He brought in a psychology book and said this book helped explain how to handle people. "If I understand it, you will be superfluous." He became furious, complaining that the therapist did not teach him psychology, and the therapist asked, "Suppose I teach you psychology, what will there be in it for me?" Harry replied that the therapist would not get anything from him because he did not want to give the therapist anything at all.

After forty interviews, Harry became able to be freer in divulging personal material. He spoke about his dreams, his sexual urges, his difficulties at school, his arguments with his mother. He joined two clubs; he attended school regularly and enjoyed going to school; and he talked more about his fear of being different from other children, his nausea, vomiting, his instinctual drives, particularly his concern about masturbation and his voyeuristic impulses. At home the situation improved considerably. As Harry explained, "I used to fight Mother because I had to let off steam and give expression to my energies in some way. Now I try to understand myself." Occasionally he would still spit at his mother, but he had given up most of his violently impulsive actions. In school, Harry came out with a medal. Among 600 graduates, ten medals were awarded and he was one of the winners.

Harry's mother[1] was a gifted person, forty-five years of age, but with many bizarre ways. She had strong hostile, aggressive feelings toward her mother, but was afraid to disobey her and was completely under her domination. Her happiest years, she claimed, were with her husband, who loved her, understood and protected her. When he died suddenly she felt lost. Her father wanted her to return to the parental home, but her mother was jealous of her husband's affection for the daughter and her son and set out to make their life a torment. She blamed her mother for Harry's problem. She was finally forced to move to a furnished room with her son. She surrounded him with constant flirtatious attention. Though sleeping in separate beds, they slept close to each other and exchanged beds on week ends. There was a fuss made by both about dressing and undressing and a constant pushing of each other on the bed. The mother often provoked fights. Then, as if in retaliation, she slapped her son, spat in his face, locked herself in the bathroom, and performed the same antics the boy did. After scenes of violence, she would write poems to Harry urging him to enter "a harmonious relationship" with her "as mother and son should have." In her interviews, she often referred to Harry's violence toward her as "a funny way to show his love," or she remarked that "he always likes to be on top of me." She was torn between "two animals, my mother and Harry." As an escape, she wrote poetry and music. She said that Harry too "can write lovely poetry and can compose music." Her bizarreness is seen in the way she explained conception and childbirth to Harry. "It is like tonsils—you don't know where they come from but the doctor takes them out!"

When the mother first came to us, she too was withdrawn from the circle of her family—sisters and brother. As treatment advanced, she resumed her social contacts, showed better control of her impulses, and was firmer with Harry. She herself felt that Harry would not have developed his present problem "if there were someone to take over when my husband died."

In summary, the predominant theme of Harry's productions was consciously that he needed insulation in order to separate himself from other people so that he himself would not be injured by their overstimulation.

[1] Treated by Betty Gabriel, Associate Therapist, Madeleine Borg Child Guidance Institute.

DISCUSSION

The withdrawal reaction as it appears from the material presented here seems to be a defense against the acting out of preoedipal and oedipal strivings both in their libidinal and destructive aspects. The child has a great need to *increase his control* of his own impulsivity sufficiently so that he can dare to feel some of it, to think some of it, and to express some of it in fantasy material initially and later in verbal material with appropriate affect. *Adequate insulation or a good protective barrier* makes this control possible. In the absence of adequate insulation, emotional withdrawal is used as a substitute.

Our study has revealed one consistent finding. An attitude of emotional reserve on the part of the therapist which was intended to be as nonstimulating as possible had the effect of making the children here reported less withdrawn in their behavior, first with the therapist and then later with other people. The verbal and play material which these children presented during their interviews suggested that they used withdrawal as a method of removing themselves from an overwhelmingly dangerous parental reality situation. In view of their inadequate protective barrier against overstimulation, they were in a two-fold danger. In the first place, parental overstimulation with inadequate insulation created a continually accumulating state of instinctual tension with concomitant states of pain, anxiety and terror. In the second place, they were continually in danger that loss of impulse control might cause behavior that would be destructive to people whom they loved and ultimately to themselves, or both situations occurred in varying degrees. The continually increasing state of instinctual tension made it increasingly desirable for them to release their tension in destructive behavior. The attempt to withdraw emotionally served a twofold purpose: if they did not feel the people around them, they were more insulated against excessive stimulation; secondly, if they did not feel the people around them, there was less of a temptation to discharge impulses toward the individuals whom their impulses might destroy.

Once these children found themselves in a comparatively healthy environment with an adult who did not stimulate them excessively, with whom their protective barrier was adequate, and with whom they could verbalize and discharge their destructive feelings in a controlled and measured way, they no longer needed to withdraw. They felt themselves to be sufficiently insulated and separated from the therapist so that they could function with greater independence of thought, feeling and action which increased their insulation. They had been rescued from the ultimate fate of the schizophrenic who, as Glover (1951) has described, "having abandoned object relations in order to avoid dangerous stimulation from the outside world and having taken steps to block reality excitations, is in the position of the child that falls asleep." *The experiencing of an insulating, protecting environment gave them a sufficient feeling of insulation to make withdrawal no longer necessary as an impulsive defensive process.*

Withdrawal then may be not only a mechanism of defense but also a protective coating designed to give the individual a period when he can gradually develop a mechanism within his personality whereby outside emotional stimulation will be kept at a minimum and will bring forth only a muffled response in harmony with the total personality.

Such additional understanding of the meaning of withdrawal should add some further direction to the therapeutic approach; namely, one should guard against too early an attempt to break the closed circle of the withdrawn child. Any attempt on the part of the therapist to further a positive relationship by showing understanding of the meaning of the patient's material too early in treatment may result in the child's showing more confusion and disorganization and thus delay or even prevent healing.

What is the social significance of an understanding of withdrawal as an attempt on the part of the child to develop a healthy insulation against an overstimulating environment? Our study suggests that it is the duty of parents, educators, therapists and caseworkers to help provide an environment for children in which they are sufficiently protected from overstimulation so that they do not need to withdraw emotionally. The need for insulation and protection in each child must be studied and understood on an individual basis. It is important that a healthy environment be provided so that in the absence of overstimulation, the child may feel free and secure enough to express a fair measure of his own creative personality and be able to function in a potentially socially useful way.

SUMMARY

1. Illustrative case material is here presented obtained during the treatment of three withdrawn children.

2. The material presented appears to demonstrate the view that emotional withdrawal is used by the unhealthy child as a substitute for an insufficient protective barrier against overstimulation.

Parental understanding, care and protection help the healthy child establish barriers against environmental pressures. These barriers serve as an insulation or protective coating. The healthy child is then able to respond to reality situations in an appropriate way with a minimum of compulsive impulsivity. In the absence of adequate insulation, the unhealthy child uses the inadequate substitute of emotional withdrawal.

3. A treatment process which is designed to help the child develop an adequate insulation against environmental pressures evidently makes the use of emotional withdrawal as a compulsive method of protection unnecessary. The child is then helped to develop toward emotional maturity.

4. Oversensitive children will need special care and understanding to protect them against overstimulation and prevent withdrawal.

BIBLIOGRAPHY

Bergman, P. & Escalona, S. (1949), Unusual Sensitivities in Very Young Children. *The Psychoanalytic Study of the Child*, 3/4:333-352. New York: International Universities Press.

Freud, S. (1922), *Beyond the Pleasure Principle*. London: Hogarth Press.

Glover, E. (1951), *Psychoanalysis: A Handbook*. London: Staples Press.

Nagelberg, L. & Spotnitz, H. (1952), Initial Steps in the Analytic Therapy of Schizophrenia in Children. *Quart. J. Child Behav.*, 4:57-65.

8

PARENTAL PERPLEXITY AND

CHILDHOOD CONFUSION

William Goldfarb, Ph.D., M.D., Lillian Sibulkin,
Marjorie Behrens, and *Hedwig Jahoda, Ph.D.*

WITHIN THE FIELD of child psychiatry, all workers have expressed an interest in the families of schizophrenic children. This interest has been motivated by the wish to clear up the etiology of the schizophrenic disorder which continues to mystify us. It is fair to say that we are still in the phase of theory-making. Hypotheses regarding the genesis of childhood schizophrenia range from those which stress biological-hereditary factors, to those which stress psychogenic-familial factors. The hereditary-biological point of view is, of course, most forcefully and completely enunciated by Lauretta Bender (1953a,b) and her colleagues (Freedman, 1954; Peck et al., 1949). They stress the underlying hereditary core with precipitation of the clinical disease by physiological crises. They postulate that there is a primary disorder within the child himself. The family is presumably important only in the determination of the child's defenses against the disintegrating effects of his "cerebral" disease. They also state there is no uniform pattern of family experience or dynamics, no gross mishandling, or conspicuously traumatic early relationship that precipitates the disease. Erikson (1950) has picturesquely described the child's defect in "sending power" with the secondary effects of this defect on the parents. The children would seem to provoke detachment in the parents.

In contrast, the psychogenic point of view sees a close connection between parental reaction and the manifestations of childhood schizophrenia. For instance, Kanner (1944, 1949,

1951) refers to the cold, obsessive, intellectualized aloofness of the parents of autistic children; Despert (1941-42, 1951) sees the maternal characteristics as aggressive, overanxious, over-solicitous, ambivalent; Mahler (1952) differentiates the symbiotic and autistic psychoses and relates these states to a disturbance in the differentiation of the child from the mother. Putnam (1951), Rank (1949, 1950) and their co-workers have postulated that there is a conspicuous maternal deprivation.

It is believed that conceptualizations of etiology and the linked therapeutic orientation significantly influence the quality and detail of one's observations. At best, methodology for the study of total family dynamics is primitive. The picture becomes even more hopeless if there is a biased unconcern with individual psychodynamics and the child's social interaction experiences within the family. In most studies, there has been a disappointing lack of careful observation and analysis of the details of the schizophrenic child's specific life experiences, his reactions and his human interactions. This is very unfortunate inasmuch as such observation is necessary for the understanding of the symptomatology even of cases of known cerebral lesion. A favorable climate, however, has been provided by the increasing therapeutic optimism and the willingness to experiment actively with a variety of therapeutic procedures. In our treatment program at the Henry Ittleson Center for Child Research the focus is on the human interaction of our children, both within the institution and also within their own families. As a result of this interest, we have admitted children from socially intact families who have agreed to participate in our therapeutic and investigative activities. We have emphasized two basic techniques for study of individual and family dynamics:

(1) A prolonged and regular contact with each parent which results in an accumulation of relevant family-oriented data and history.

(2) Planned observation of the child in interaction with various members of his family.

Applying these techniques, we have become increasingly per-
suaded that the parents of the schizophrenic children in our care
show an unusual relation to the schizophrenic child. For discussion, we have termed the observed parental pattern of behavior
"parental perplexity." The nature of parental perplexity is illustrated in the following observations of Tommy T.

(1) On a visiting day at the Center, the psychologist's attention was
arrested by this scene. Tommy was under his mother's skirt. He had
dropped his trousers and was masturbating. In addition, he was poking
at Mrs. T.'s genitals. She stood frozen and unmoving with tears in her
eyes. Pleadingly she asked the psychologist, "What shall I do?"

(2) When Tommy was at home, these observations of an actual
home visit were made:

During mealtime, it was planned that the observer would eat with
the family. Tommy was running down the stairs, walked in and out
of the living room several times to the kitchen. The observer accompanied Tommy to the kitchen. Tommy took a handful of Jello out of
a bowl as he passed it, pushed some of the Jello into his mouth and
dropped the rest of the bowl on the floor as he went out of the kitchen.
There was no intervention by the parents. He then opened the back
door, and Mrs. T. said to the observer that he wanted to go out. It had
snowed the night before, and Mrs. T. explained to Tommy that he
had to put his coat and boots on. Mr. T. went for his clothes, urged
him to put his coat on, but Tommy ignored him. He went directly to
the car outside with the father running after him. When Tommy came
back with his father, he walked into the kitchen, picked up a slice of
fish from a plate, stuffed it in his mouth and dropped the rest on the
floor. Mrs. T. immediately picked the fish off the floor. Mr. T. took
Tommy's outer clothes off. As soon as they had been removed, Tommy
made for the front door and went out. Both parents chased after him
again with his clothes. A few minutes later Tommy ran back into the
house with his father following. Mr. T. wanted to take Tommy's
jacket off, but Tommy would not let him. Instead, he walked around
the kitchen and dining room taking food off the plates and dropping
it on the floor. Mrs. T. said in a reasonable fashion that he was hungry
and prepared a plate of food for him. Tommy was out of the house
again with Mr. T. after him. When Tommy came back, Mrs. T. said
to him she understood he was hungry. She urged him to sit at the table.
He sat there for a few minutes, ate from a plate, dropped food on the
floor, got up, walked around the table, took food from the other plates
on the table, pushed the food into his mouth and dropped the rest on

the table or on the floor. This occurred repeatedly during the next hour. As Mrs. T. saw him do it, she scolded him in a calm, sweet voice and explained each time that his plate was on the table, that the food was for everyone, not just for him. Tommy just ignored her. When Tommy put his hand on the wine decanter, his father offered him some wine, but Tommy ignored him. Tommy ran out of the house and Mrs. T. said, "Go after him, he is not properly dressed." Her husband quickly did what she asked.

We have supplied two discrete events which typify every moment of interaction between Tommy and his parents. In his random explorations, Tommy is faced with an environment that is totally amorphous and unorganized. His experience is ambiguous and unstructured. At no point do the parents offer direction or control in a spontaneous and assertive way. They "run after" the child, so to speak, as he moves about aimlessly. They do not intervene to break up, or to control, the boundless fluidity of his behavior. The mother is dominant in the situation and requires that the father and the other children submissively meet her unorganized pattern of behavior with the child. Mr. T. merely perpetuates the ambiguity of Tommy's human environment. The family tone, therefore, is set primarily by the mother. Similarly, the aberrant family setting for Tommy reflects a deviation in the execution of maternal function. The parents show a persistent, exhausting concentration on, and for, Tommy. Mrs. T. even has the magical belief that she has special capacity to communicate with Tommy and to understand his needs. Yet in actual fact, she seems inadequate in achieving genuine empathy with the child. She does not seem to know what he needs at the moment that he needs it. For example, she offers him an abundance of food with the remark, "I can tell he is hungry." The food she encourages into his mouth immediately slips out of his loose mouth to the floor. Mrs. T.'s behavior is like that of a mother who mechanically plays with her baby in accord with a rule for maternal behavior at a time when he needs to be relieved of his wet, chafing diaper. The unusual nature of Mrs. T.'s relation to Tommy is most dramatically seen when he is destructive, or aggressive, or involved in acts which challenge the average individual's characteristic reaction formations, such as indiscriminate soiling, masturbation, fingering his anus, or smearing his food. The usual response of his mother is a persistent, hollow, sweet smile or total bewilderment.

In brief, here are some salient facts in Tommy's history, and the psychodynamic conclusions drawn from our total contact with the family. Tommy was referred to the Center at the age of six by a child guidance clinic to which Mrs. T. had originally gone. Mrs. T. sought help because she found it difficult to comprehend or relate to Tommy. The onset of the illness was put at age three and a half. Up to then he was presumably bright and well developed, although continued contact with the family revealed that for some time before this incident Tommy had also been withdrawn and disturbing. Precipitating circumstances included a very tense household in which Mrs. T. felt criticized by her mother-in-law. In a state of desperation and temper, Mrs. T. gave up Tommy entirely to the care of his paternal grandmother.

The grandmother was constantly correcting, disciplining and disapproving of Tommy. After three days, Tommy became extremely hyperactive and cried incessantly. He became frightened of airplane noises. He wanted only to be in his mother's lap. He stopped speaking and felt her eyes and ears with his hands. At the time of referral, there was no speech at all. Tommy was hyperactive, demanded his mother's attention, went into temper tantrums if she gave any attention to a younger baby. He was quick and agile. In a few moments he would upset everything in the house, pulling out drawers, throwing things around the rooms. He needed constant supervision. There was an extreme preoccupation with cars and a persistent effort to get into unlocked cars. He could not be permitted outdoors alone. He frequently would cover his ears with his hands. He never had a full meal at any time but would eat frequently during the day. He would spill food over himself and the house.

Tommy was unwanted and unplanned for, but the mother insists she was pleased with him after his birth. He weighed seven pounds at birth. Mrs. T. describes him as a helpless baby who lay with his eyes closed. She contrasted him with her youngest baby who "opened her eyes to see the world." Mr. T. was himself hospitalized at this time for an arthritic condition and was invalided for a year. For the week following their return from the hospital, Mrs. T. cared for her husband while Tommy was cared for by a nurse. Mrs. T. recalls her irritation because she was not strong enough to care for both. According to Mrs. T., Mr. T. "did not open his heart up to Tommy." He would not respond to the baby when it was put in his lap. When Tommy came home he could not urinate easily, cried and was tense. Mrs. T. recalls also that Tommy had "colic" as a baby. Tommy was given a bottle every hour or two because it was felt that he could drink only a little at a time. He frequently vomited the milk. Mrs. T. said she was always patient and spent much of her time feeding Tommy. Tommy was able to take normal amounts of food at about six months of age. At three years he fed himself and "ate like a little gentleman." Tommy was bowel-trained at nine months and stopped wetting early, although the exact age was unknown. He lost control of his sphincters with onset of his acute disease at the age of three and a half. He walked at one year and talked before he walked. At three years of age he spoke in full sentences and was completely comprehensible. As noted, there was a rapid loss of speech function at three and a half years. Mrs. T. recalls that Tommy was always "weakish" and easily frightened, inclined to be withdrawn but also loving and affectionate. With the onset of the disease at three and a half, he masturbated openly. Tommy had always been shy with children, but at three and a half was openly fearful in their presence.

Mrs. T. was born in Europe and was the oldest of ten children. She describes her father as a successful, gregarious business man who liked to have company around and who was inclined to pay more attention to company than to his children. Mrs. T.'s mother was distant and unaffectionate. As a child, Mrs. T. was compliant and "so sensitive and gentle that she always fainted." Although Jewish, she was sent to a convent to learn handwork and how to become a lady. In her words, she learned a "genial acceptance of responsibilities." She was given and accepted maternal responsibilities at a young age. When twelve years old, she recalls intervening, in adult fashion, in a physical struggle between her father and one of his employees.

She is an intelligent, articulate individual who smiles in a tense, rigid, persistent fashion. She feels herself to be a very strong person. She expresses great expectations and high ideals. She feels people should accept things stoically. She sometimes feels "impotent and helpless" but is annoyed that she is not stronger. "I steel myself when there is trouble, then I have no feelings at all. I stiffen and straighten out." She must always be serving others and sees herself as the all-giving mother. She is deeply religious. There is a dissociated quality in her magical omnipotent feelings of closeness to God. She has great difficulty in admitting weakness. She talks of Tommy as a psychologist would, and has given very thorough written descriptions of his behavior. Her attitude is one of resigned willingness to perform her special function with Tommy in a belief that she alone can bring him out of his illness.

Mr. T. is less well known to us. He has always been the passive parent. He acknowledges all his wife's values and meets her demands at home. He is a very intelligent person and successful in his job of teaching. He seems depressed, cries when he speaks of his father's death, and is very anxious about the possibility of his mother dying.

We now have had fairly intensive contact with the family for over a year. We have been interested particularly in the psychodynamics of Mrs. T.'s performance as a mother. Mrs. T. seemed to have had very little in the way of direct emotional response from her mother. She was required to grow up precociously and act as a parent both to her own parents and to her other siblings. All through her life, she has denied her own spontaneous wishes and her rage at frustration of these wishes. Instead, there has been a compensatory need to believe in her own superior ability to mother and care for others. Nevertheless, she possesses an unusual amount of rage plus an unconscious belief in her omnipotence and her potentially destructive powers. There is a consequent denial of her rage with resultant inability to be spontaneous and an outer façade of smiling, detached tolerance, combined with the air of frozen bewilderment that we have described.

DISCUSSION

Perplexity occurs to some degree in every parent. It may represent the average uncertainty of any individual learning a new task. This is seen commonly in the young mother with her first-born, or with new counselors at the residential center. Hilde Bruch (1952) and others have pointed to a culturally determined uncertainty among middle-class parents today. Presumably these parents have been robbed of their spontaneity because they have been frightened by the flood of professional warnings and enjoinders given them. The parent who is anything but totally permissive is made to suffer pangs of guilt. Finally, there is the universal uncertainty of a parent faced with any kind of illness or disability in her child.

We have applied the term parental perplexity to a special type of parental response. We have observed that parental perplexity is especially characteristic of parents of schizophrenic children under our observation. With these parents, the response is far beyond normal expectations. Further, the parents possess an underlying psychodynamic core which predisposes them to this extreme behavior. When observed, parental perplexity in the parents of our schizophrenic children combines several elements:

(1) Outwardly, there is a striking lack of organized parental activity. The parents are outstandingly passive and uncertain. They do not stand out from the environment and are hollowly bland.

(2) There is a lack of parental spontaneity, and a lack of immediate natural awareness of the child's needs for gratification. The parent performs mechanically the parental tasks without ability to empathize with the child.

(3) When pressed by the bizarreness or destructive nature of the child's symptoms, the mother gives overt signs of bewilderment. Often these are verbalized as, "I don't know what to do," or "Tell me what to do."

(4) The child reacts as though there were no controls, either outer or inner. One sees perseverative, uncontrolled aimlessness, confusion, and uncontained and enduring emergency responses of fear and rage.

There is a quality of specificity to the perplexity reaction, in that the parents show varying degrees of perplexity response to the different siblings. Parental perplexity is most extreme with the schizophrenic child.

In its immediate impact on the schizophrenic child, the atmosphere of the families studied appears to be mother-dominated. Often, as in the T. family, the father and siblings become extensions of the mother and elaborate her reaction pattern with the disturbed child. In other families, the father's relationship to the mother acts to exaggerate her perplexity with the child. In still others, the father is unable to counteract the impact of the mother.

We have been able to study the psychodynamic structure of the mothers best of all. Underlying the above-described bewilderment appears to be an immense reservoir of repressed rage toward the schizophrenic child. Sometimes this rage emerges explosively for brief intervals. More usually it is diverted in retroflexed fashion into a state of clinical depression. Equally important is the mother's unconscious wishful image of her omnipotent magical power. Murderous rage is thus combined with an unconscious belief in her catastrophically destructive powers. Any move toward the child is potentially capable of destroying the child. (Persistent fear of the child's death is extremely common in this group.) The mother inhibits her rage and becomes blocked in the execution of her mothering role. We have sought to explore clinically the basis for the mother's unconscious rage toward her schizophrenic child and her continued fantasy of personal omnipotence. Uniformly, the mothers themselves seemed to have had early infantile experiences of affective deprivation at the hands of their own mothers. Frustration occurred at the oral-nutritional level, at which state normal infants usually achieve magical gratification by the mother. This deprivation is the probable basis for what Rank (1949, 1950) and others have called the narcissism of the mothers of schizophrenic children. The mothers themselves are helplessly caught in their own dependency needs and are preoccupied with fantasies of omnipotence and effortless gratification. This is true of those mothers who present a patent and outward picture of total helplessness and dependency. It is equally true of the mothers who hide their deep sucking needs under a disguise of exaggerated overcompensated concentration on their maternal functions.[1] When the child, who later becomes schizophrenic, is born, the mother experiences him as a monstrous challenge to her own needs for infantile gratification. She cannot bring herself to empathize spontaneously with the child's minimal needs for protection and care.[2] The demands of the new child for quick gratification assails the frustrated mother's own omnipotence, and she feels overpowering rage. As noted, the overcompensated inhibition of the rage results in what we have called parental perplexity. We need to test out further our impression that in most of our histories the unconscious rage seems to have preceded the mother's awareness of the child's illness as such. Fear of the child's death was common in the maternal histories, even at the moment of delivery of the child.

[1] We have had occasion to psychoanalyze a perplexed mother of this kind. She literally nursed her baby all day long and told of having nursed her baby for as long as four to five hours at a time. Her own major and dominating fantasy was that of consuming the maternal breast.

[2] Mrs. T. did not stop Tommy and watched him helplessly as he climbed to the garage attic and finally hung down dangerously from the window ledge high in the air.

Out of our special interest in the interrelationship between repressed omnipotent strivings and outer parental perplexity, we have looked for similar patterns of reaction in our counselors. Repeatedly the relationship has been confirmed. For example, the following incident came to our attention. Before beginning a case conference, it was casually noted that one of the counselors had a painful finger. Somewhat reluctantly she permitted the clinical director to look at the finger. The finger was swollen and blue and there was an obvious fracture. On inquiry, the counselor admitted that the injury had occurred about four hours previously in the arts and crafts shop. One of the aggressive children had been very disruptive to the group. At one point when the counselor tried to restrain him from throwing an object, the object hit her finger. The next day, about thirty hours later, we held another conference. This time the counselor said she wanted to raise a question regarding her handling of the incident with the boy. Should she let him know that he had injured her? We were taken aback at the remarkable control and passivity of the counselor, and asked her if there had been any pain. She denied this entirely. On inquiry, she affirmed her fear of letting the boy know he had hit her because she did not want to increase his anxiety. She denied steadfastly any resentment toward the boy.

It is hypothesized that the complex parental pattern we have called parental perplexity and the parallel disorganization of the child's psychological surroundings have serious consequences for the child. It is believed that they contribute to the confused mental state of the schizophrenic child. This is especially true of his problem in orienting himself to his own body and in differentiating himself from his outer reality. Time and space orientation are also affected. The child has no definitive guides for action, no way of learning bounds, no basis for control of motility. He cannot know what to expect. The parental passivity and detachment destroy the foundation for internalization of a defined parental image. There is no clear-cut prototype or design for achieving control and a system of either painful or pleasurable anticipations. The emergency emotions of rage and fear can become overwhelming and unmanageable to the child himself. Also what is normally accepted as a reward is not received as such by these children.

Regardless of the etiology of childhood schizophrenia, the schizophrenic child deserves and requires an organized and directed environment as much as, perhaps more than, the normal. In treatment we have become impressed with the slow albeit partial, definite reversibility of the child's confusional pattern. This seems to occur in an atmosphere of benevolent certainty, where there is a consistent twenty-four hour adult interaction and intervention with and for the child. We have had an example, too, of a child in partial recovery becoming disorganized and psychotic in the specific presence of a counselor whose behavior and underlying psychodynamics were similar to those attributed to the mothers of schizophrenic children.

With parents of schizophrenic children, the following simple principles are helpful. An active, authoritative role with the parents is assumed and we cut through directly to the parents' fear of their own aggression. The objective is to diminish their ambivalence and frozen indecisiveness so as to get them to react with normal assertiveness to the child's behavior. In one way or another, the formula is communicated: "Put bounds on the child's behavior. Introduce normal expectations. Do not worry so about hurting the child. No single act of yours will be permanently and catastrophically dangerous to the child."

This may be illustrated in the following brief incidents. Robert, an eight-year-old schizophrenic boy, was waiting with his mother for the doctor. As the doctor came into the waiting room, Robert was punching his mother viciously in the face with the full weight of his body. She sat with unflinching passivity, indeed, without any expression at all. The therapist asked in a firm loud voice that both the mother and child could hear, "Why do you permit Robert to beat you up so?" The mother and child both looked up quite startled, but the beating had stopped. The mother asked, "What should I do?" The therapist answered unhesitatingly, "Stop him, of course." Later Robert's mother admitted she became aware at that moment of how angry she had been for years over the beatings the boy had administered to her.

Another mother came for office consultation with her nine-year-old boy, Harry. Harry was found in her lap, pressing roughly up against her. Repeatedly and without immediate provocation, he jabbed both elbows with all his strength into his mother's breasts. The mother sat unmoving. The doctor asked why she permitted Harry to hurt her and she in turn asked the usual question, "What should I do?" Our direction, of course, was not to permit him to hurt her. Subsequently the direct physical attacks on this mother stopped. The symptomatic relief in both parent and child has sometimes been dramatic. The rationale essentially is to buttress and protect the parent. Thereby her wishes for infantile gratification and dependency are met. Her self-estimation is enhanced, while at the same time she assuages her guilt by assigning the assertiveness with the child to the therapist rather than to herself. More organized management of the child thus becomes possible.

BIBLIOGRAPHY

Bender, L. (1953a), Childhood Schizophrenia. *Psychiat. Quart.*, 27:663-681.
—— (1953b), Evidences from Studies of Childhood Schizophrenia. *A.M.A. Arch. Neurol. & Psychiat.*, 70:535.
Bruch, H. (1952), *Don't Be Afraid of Your Child*. New York: Farrar, Straus & Young.
Despert, J. (1941-42), Prophylactic Aspect of Schizophrenia in Childhood. *Nerv. Child*, 1:199-231.
—— (1951), Some Considerations Relating to the Genesis of Autistic Behavior in Children. *Am. J. Orthopsychiat.*, 21:335-350.
Erikson, E. H. (1950), *Childhood and Society*. New York: W. W. Norton & Co.
Freedman, A. M. (1954), Maturation and Its Relation to the Dynamics of Childhood Schizophrenia. *Am. J. Orthopsychiat.*, 24:487-491.
Kanner, L. (1944), Early Infantile Autism. *J. Pediat.*, 25:211-217.
—— (1949), Problems of Nosology and Psychodynamics of Early Infantile Autism. *Am. J. Orthopsychiat.*, 19:416-426.

—— (1951), A Discussion of Early Infantile Autism. *Dig. Neurol. & Psychiat.,* 19:158.

Mahler, M. (1952), On Child Psychosis and Schizophrenia. Autistic and Symbiotic Infantile Psychoses. *The Psychoanalytic Study of the Child,* 7:286-305. New York: International Universities Press.

Peck, H. B., Rabinovitch, R. D., & Cramer, J. B. (1949), A Treatment Program for Parents of Schizophrenic Children. *Am. J. Orthopsychiat.,* 19:592-598.

Putnam, M. C., Rank, B., & Kaplan, S. (1951), Notes on John G. A. Case of Primal Depression in an Infant. *The Psychoanalytic Study of the Child,* 6:38-58. New York: International Universities Press.

Rank, B. (1949), Adaptation of the Psychoanalytic Technique for the Treatment of Young Children with Atypical Development. *Am. J. Orthopsychiat.,* 19:130-139.

Rank, B., & MacNaughton, D. (1950), A Clinical Contribution to Early Ego Development. *The Psychoanalytic Study of the Child,* 5:53-65. New York: International Universities Press.

A PROBLEM OF EGO ORGANIZATION
IN A LATENCY CHILD

Report of a Clinical Conference

IN 1954-55 THE Madeleine Borg Child Guidance Institute held a series of so-called Interdisciplinary Meetings, attended by the psychiatrists, psychologists and casework supervisors on its staff. The purpose of these meetings was to clarify certain problems regarding intake policies which had arisen as a result of changes in diagnostic thinking and in the character of the problems being referred to the Child Guidance Institute for treatment. This series of meetings concluded with the presentation of the case of a nine-year-old girl for whom residential treatment had been recommended by a staff psychiatrist but who was taken on for treatment on an exploratory basis. It was intended to utilize the material from this case as a basis for the determination of definitive policies for handling borderline and psychotic children.

Though originally planned for only one meeting, so extensive did the discussion of this case become and so manifold were the problems it raised, both diagnostically and administratively, that it was prolonged over three. We present here an edited transcript of these meetings in order to illustrate some of the difficulties encountered in approaching such a case and to set forth what we regard as a provocative and fascinating clinical discussion.

Though the fundamental question posed about the case— "Shall we or shall we not accept such a case for treatment in the Child Guidance Institute?"—is not definitively answered, the questions raised in the discussion led to the establishment of a research project in the treatment of certain types of schizo-

phrenic children, for the purpose of more precise determination
of criteria for the acceptance of such children for treatment.

Participants in Clinical Conference

Dr. Maurice R. Friend, Clinical Director, Madeleine Borg Child
 Guidance Institute, Chairman
Dr. Joachim Flescher, Assistant Clinical Director, Madeleine
 Borg Child Guidance Institute
Hilde Adelberg, Associate Therapist
Dr. Ednita Bernabeu, Consultant Psychiatrist
Dr. Peter Blos, Consultant in Psychotherapy
Dr. Aaron H. Esman, Consultant Psychiatrist
Mrs. Yonata Feldman, Borough Supervisor
Margaret Galdston, Psychiatric Caseworker
Naomi Grossman, Psychiatric Caseworker
Betty Klein, Supervisor
Mrs. Etta Kolodney, Casework Supervisor
Mrs. Bettina Lehnert, Assistant Borough Supervisor
Leah Levinger, Acting Chief Psychologist
Sidney Love, Associate Therapist
Dr. Harry Luloff, Consultant Psychiatrist
Dr. Andrée Royon, Consultant in Psychotherapy
Oscar Sternbach, Consultant in Psychotherapy
Mrs. Liselott Toby, Chief Psychiatric Social Worker
Kathryn Werner, Senior Psychologist

I

CASE PRESENTATION

MISS GALDSTON: The client is a girl of nine who was first seen at the agency one year ago. She is the younger of two siblings. Her mother, a housewife, is thirty-five, and her father, a salesman, forty-three. They were referred to the Madeleine Borg Child Guidance Institute by a psychiatrist to whom they had previously been referred by the family physician. The mother complained that the child had been showing "strange reactions" virtually since birth. She showed no affection toward her parents, but was almost promiscuously affectionate toward strangers. She was willful and disobedient, full of fears. She feared the dark, she feared stairs, she had anticipatory fears about accidents. Even before she could walk she had been fearful that she would fall. She frequently would sing at the top of her lungs, and the mother interpreted this as a defense against her fears. From the age of eight months she had been a chronic thumb-sucker.

At some undetermined point in her life she had begun having recurrent headaches and vomiting, but these had decreased in frequency about a year before the patient was first seen. The most dramatic complaint, however, was her preoccupation with dogs. She talked and fantasied about dogs continually. She had dogs and other children as imaginary playmates. At school she was described as aggressive, and averse to proximity to other children. She had to be the leader in activities or she would withdraw completely.

Disturbances pervaded the *developmental history*. The patient was born four years after her older brother; the mother

173

had had a miscarriage two years earlier. The pregnancy had been uneventful except for slight staining during the third month. The child was born prematurely at the beginning of the ninth month, weighing only five pounds. She was breast-fed for two weeks, then placed on the bottle. At eight months she refused the bottle and the cup, and had to be entirely spoon-fed, to the great annoyance of the mother. Finally at two, the mother threatened to refuse entirely to feed her, and the patient accepted cup feeding thereafter. She has eaten well since, but now has great anxiety about missing meals.

Toilet-training was instituted at eight months and bowel control was achieved quickly. Wetting, however, continued until the age of three and a half, and occasional night wettings have persisted during periods of illness. The patient is now quite fearful about wetting. She walked and talked at about two, with talking coming first. Her first steps were taken toward a dog. Her parents feared that she was retarded and took her to a physician. During the examination she had a spell of some kind, in which her head went back and her eyes rolled about. This was attributed to eye muscle weakness, and she was given glasses. Almost immediately she began to masturbate, using her glasses, toys, or the arms of furniture. This continued until she was four, when her mother told her she'd harm herself if she continued. She stopped, "more or less."

At four the patient began school, and was a problem from the start. She was aggressive, striking out at other children and insisting on being the leader. The mother was referred by the school to a family agency, and was seen there for one year, with the therapy concentrated on her relationship with her husband.

The patient loved dogs from an early age. At four her parents bought a dog which had "poor bladder control." They tired of the dog after five or six months and got rid of him; almost immediately the patient began to want to be a dog, barking, refusing to talk and crawling about on all fours. Simultaneously she expressed wishes to be a boy, refusing to wear dresses and making efforts to urinate standing up. The family "cured" her of her wish to be a dog by presenting her one evening with a bowl of dog food while the family ate all her favorite things for dinner, then pretended to call the dogcatcher. They tried to stress the positive aspects of femininity for her and felt that this had some effect.

Medical history was unremarkable except for recurrent severe headaches which began at some undetermined age and decreased in frequency about a year before she was first seen. She had fairly frequent colds, and would vomit whenever she was ill.

The *family background* was that of a fairly prosperous middle-class family who, however, all slept in one bedroom. The parents were certain that the children never saw them having intercourse. The mother described the family as "semi-religious." She had kept a kosher home at first, but stopped after a few years.

The *mother,* Mrs. Davis, was non-Jewish by birth, but converted to Judaism upon her marriage. She was an only child, and her mother and father were divorced when she was a year and a half old. She lived with her grandparents and various relatives until twelve, seeing her mother only on week ends, when she had to share her with her men friends. When she was twelve, her mother married a man who had two children of his own. This marriage lasted only two years, and the maternal grandmother left, taking the patient's mother with her, and came to New York. Here the patient's mother (now fourteen) got jobs modeling and went on double dates with her mother, who preferred people to think they were sisters. The maternal grandmother did not marry again until the patient's mother had herself married (at seventeen).

The *father* was the second of six children; his father is dead, but his mother is still living. His wife described him as an unaffectionate person who "makes love by the clock" and gives little to his children.

The patient was seen for a *diagnostic interview by a staff psychiatrist.* She appeared quite prepared for the interview, coming in readily and beginning to play with dolls. She created a scene between a baby and a father in which the father wanted to take a bath, but the baby jumped in. The father reprimanded the baby, whereupon the baby screamed. This was all done with appropriate voice changes and great dramatization. She then wanted to draw and sing, drawing a house and grass and singing at the top of her lungs. "Miss Galdston," she said, "has a girl who sings so loud she can't talk"—but she denied that this was herself. She drew a figure, starting from the bottom and ending with the face, in which she put no features other than the eyes.

She then told a story about her drawing of a house and a girl. A dog was biting the girl. The dog was drawn with fangs, and with the legs growing from the head. She then drew a detached body. She said she liked dogs and dreamed of them; in one such dream she was a big police dog who climbed a tree. The dog fell but was unhurt. She told of the dog her parents got rid of because it barked; her mother was made nervous and her father got so angry he'd have choked the dog. The psychiatrist noted that the child was very alert for any sign of affect or response from the examiner. While she questioned the mother, the patient sat in the waiting room and sang at the top of her lungs. The mother seemed terribly anxious about the child, but was self-protective, making it clear how much she had done to correct the child's bizarreness. She was not able to tell anything about herself.

The *psychiatrist's impression* was that of a probably psychotic child, with ego disorganization, but with strong defensive efforts to hold herself together. She suggested that therapy might be tried, but indicated that institutional treatment might ultimately prove necessary.

The therapist, in her first interview with the child, was impressed by her resemblance to the mother, of whom she appeared a coarser version. She was very active, constantly exploring, using toys, talking and singing. She showed no overt fear, and preferred to have her mother wait outside. She didn't know why she was coming, but spoke of her bad dreams, in one of which she feared that "foxes" would get her. While drawing a girl near a tree and house she sang, loudly and well, "The Star-Spangled Banner." She said she thought the therapist was the prettiest lady she had ever seen, or at least been able to talk to. She finger-painted with no hesitation, using the paint tactilely rather than expressively, and with no concern about soiling. The final mixture of colors looked "like blood." As she cleaned up, she moved her body rhythmically back and forth while singing and giggling in a manner suggestive of autoerotic activity.

In a subsequent interview, following the psychiatric interview, the patient indicated that she wanted to play house with a clay dog. She chose mother, father and baby dolls, a toilet, a bathtub and a bathinette. She began a long play sequence, using different voices for each individual and another voice, her own, for narrative purposes. She put the baby doll on the toilet, saying it was "doing its duty." The doll fell off and in doing so spread its "duty" all over the floor. Here she made some "duty" of brown clay and dropped it into the toilet. The mother and father screamed at the baby saying it was dirty and filthy. Following this there was an orgy of wild toilet play in which the mother fell into the toilet, saying "I'm going to kill you." The baby was saved by the dog. The parents then yelled and beat the baby until she learned to make "duty" properly. Then the baby fell into the "duty." The baby then disguised herself as a puppy so that the parents wouldn't know who she was.

DISCUSSION

Miss Levinger: This child functions very unevenly. At one moment she will behave like an adolescent, and then like a primitive child, and then like a normal eight-year-old. This is a sign of serious pathology. She also shows extensive disturbances in perception, marked by fragmentation and distortion in her drawings, which are, however, generally quite mature.

Mr. Love: I wonder if we could find anything in the mother that could have brought about this child's disturbance. Considering the presumably traumatic effect of early toilet-training at eight months, the traumatic separation from the dog at four, and the mother's own traumatic separation experience at one and a half, it seems that there might be reactive factors that would be amenable to treatment; the child has suffered severe oral deprivation and has turned to animals as a substitute for the mother. More data regarding the mother-child relationship are needed.

Miss Grossman: In view of the intense symbiosis of mother and child, would one interview a week be sufficient to treat this child? Also, wouldn't residential treatment really be necessary to treat this child who is so disturbed? How autistic must a child be to need residential treatment?

Dr. Friend: At this point I'd like to clarify the concept of autism. There are certainly indications that this child is not autistic; for example, her awareness of her audience. Autistic children are resistive to any environmental relationships or are unable to communicate. This child is certainly not like that. The question really is, "If the schizophrenic child is not autistic, what are the therapeutic considerations?"

Dr. Luloff: I should suggest the following points: (1) Can the community, that is, the schools, etc., contain the child? (2) Can the child benefit from treatment? (3) What is the nature of the mother's pathology in her relationship with the child? Can she change? All these questions must be answered in the affirmative before the child can be taken on for ambulatory treatment.

Dr. Friend: We must also consider our own capacity to deal with such types of disturbance. To determine the suitability of the child for help in a child guidance clinic we must formulate the presenting picture of the individual child; whether the pathology is reactive or not is not the determining criterion. In this instance there is no question of a social emergency. As to the positive factors, I wonder whether the child's reference to the worker as "the prettiest lady I have ever seen" is really a positive factor or is something else.

Dr. Bernabeu: I'd like to turn to the question of the child's toilet-training. I wonder whether it was really sadistic or consistent with the norms of the cultural group. Also, I want to emphasize the distinction between reactive and projective reactions of the child: there were hints in the fantasy material of the problem of separation of the body from the feces, that is, fear of loss of part of the self which is equated with being killed. This would represent an intrapsychic rather than a reactive mechanism.

Dr. Friend: I have some question about this. I think that the problem here is one of a very primitive anxiety unrelated to castration or separation anxiety and far more diffuse and apparent.

Dr. Flescher: I must demur from the trend of the discussion at this point. We should not be discussing dynamics yet; we should be concentrating on the description of the pathology and a delineation of the positive resources of the child.

Dr. Friend: Certainly the child should be evaluated descriptively; whether the pathology is reactive or not is not the determining criterion as to suitability of the child for treatment in the CGI. I think, though, that consideration of dynamic factors is inevitable in the evaluation of the child.

Dr. Esman: May I add that the fact that we can understand a case dynamically does not mean that we can necessarily reverse the pathology.

Mrs. Lehnert: Certainly it is always necessary that we assess the strengths as well as the weaknesses. In this case, however, there is a lack of repressive forces, and the unconscious is too much on the surface; for example, the child's apparent awareness of the reason for identification with dogs.

Dr. Friend: I want to develop that point. The dog complex gives us access to the child's use of primary processes of identification which are not warded off by the conscious ego. We are susceptible to such children because their emotional lability enables them to identify with us so readily. On the other hand, there is a part of this child's ego which is not so deeply involved. She shows considerable ability to conform with reality demands.

Dr. Blos: I'm impressed by the fragmentation of the child's ego. She concedes to external objects functions of what should be inner psychic structure. She projects part of her superego onto animals, in a totemistic defense. The dog is the object of fear and at the same time a source of protection. Such fragmentation is the result of inadequate identification with the mother. Nevertheless, the pathology must be seen against the background of the child's integrative capacities. She seems to have some retention of superego. Her drawings show grasp of form and proportion. This is not a case of complete psychotic surrender.

Dr. Friend: Nonetheless, the child's behavior is inappropriate. She handles the interview like a much younger child. Whatever is happening in relation to the mother, the child has functioned with difficulty in object relationships virtually since birth, and her ego functions show impairment in a number of areas. For instance, school performance is poor even though the child is at her grade level. There is a history of impairment of motor development, with difficulty in walking in the absence of demonstrable organic pathology and the reversal of the normal developmental sequences, in that she talked before she could walk.

Miss Klein: Yes, but there was great pressure from the mother throughout.

Dr. Friend: In addition, there is the child's difficulty in social relationships in which she has to be the boss or she withdraws.

Dr. Flescher: But this last point is not typical for schizophrenic children. We find such alternatives also in well-defined character disorders and in the behavior disorders of younger children.

Dr. Friend: There are also indications of erotization associated with the child's screaming. This is highly suggestive of autoerotic activity. At this juncture, though, I'd like to raise the question of the strengths in the patient's personality.

Miss Galdston: First, there is the child's effort to differentiate part of herself from her fantasies and impulses, as indicated by her role of narrator. In addition, there is her ability to play something out and then relate it to circumstances at home, although at times in the relationship with me, she talked to a fantasy dog.

Dr. Bernabeu: In that connection I recall the case of a four-and-a-half-year-old schizophrenic child who identified with a dog. The present patient, however, does not merely identify with the dog, but uses him as a protective monster. This is closer to primitive unconscious processes. The fact, however, that she elaborates the dog as an outside protector suggests that she has had some experiences of protection in her life, which she can use to hold herself together and which can be used in therapy.

Dr. Friend: Let's summarize the material to this point. It seems to me that many of the supposed strengths really represent restitutive efforts to make up for a schizophrenic break. Let me raise two questions: (1) Is the break here really a relatively complete one, with a natural mobilization of adaptive tools? (2) Since the child is deeply regressed, what is her capacity to respond to therapy and to reverse the regression?

Mr. Love: The child's apparent efforts to appreciate the reality of the interview situation certainly bespeak some reversibility.

Dr. Friend: To conclude the discussion, I'd like some expressions of opinion concerning the advisability of treating the child in the Child Guidance Institute as opposed to referral of the case for residential treatment.

Dr. Royon: I feel that the child could possibly be treated because of her apparent strengths.

Mrs. Feldman: I would accept her for treatment, with an expectant attitude which does not exclude ultimate residential placement.

Mrs. Toby: I favor accepting her, despite my opinion at the time of the screening interview that residential treatment was indicated. I agree that residential treatment may still prove necessary and the family should be prepared in advance for such a possibility.

Dr. Friend: I feel strongly that the child should not be treated in the Child Guidance Institute, because of the indications of primary-process breakthroughs into consciousness and the extensive disturbance of object relationships. Perhaps as a research project or as an unusual situation of some kind, such a case might be taken on, but not as a matter of policy. We do not know enough about the intrapsychic adjustment in this sort of child. The Child Guidance Institute should restrict its services to children with greater ego strength than this patient shows.

We shall continue the discussion of this case at our next meeting.

II

DISCUSSION

Dr. Flescher: I want to resume discussion of the case with particular emphasis on the difficulties which may be presented by the problem of an initial impression of schizophrenia, with a consequent *a priori* decision not to accept such cases for treatment. I intend to point out the existence of certain strengths in this child. First, however, I think we should discuss the psychological tests.

Miss Werner: The child's behavior during testing was as has been described, with loud singing, etc. Though at times sulky, she was able to accept reality in the test situation. Many features indicated psychosis, among them fluidity and pressure of ideas, need for fantasy, much self-reference, perseveration and contamination of ideas, and a great deal of unevenness. Ego boundaries were weak, with a poorly defined body image. She showed, however, awareness of acceptable norms and an adequate grasp at times when her fantasies were not stimulated. There was some evidence of the development of compulsive defenses, but real conformity strivings appeared weak. Intelligence was average or above, but usable only on verbal levels (I.Q. 89, Verbal

100, Performance 78). There had been little change since the previous test of 1951, and although marked increases in ego controls had occurred, the child was still impulsive. Body image showed maturation. Dogs appeared in all the drawings; the image of the dog was on a higher level than that of the human figure. The interest in dogs seemed to be a product of a body-mind dichotomy, with the dog seen as a symbol of body needs and strivings which are unacceptable in humans. The child was able to go through the motions of communication, but she was too self-absorbed for real relationships. She appeared to be dealing with reality on a borderline basis.

However, her weaknesses were seen as marginal and the data did not suggest that institutional placement was necessary. Ego strength seemed better than one would expect of a schizophrenic child of this age.

Dr. Friend: In the search for assets and deficits, psychological data may be of value. Here we see indications of disturbance in every sphere. Can we abstract from these data anything about assets and liabilities?

Miss Klein: It should be noted that the mother was in casework treatment between the child's two tests, with emphasis on marital problems and on guidance in the handling of the child. The indications that the mother can profit from treatment are hopeful, since any treatment of the child will necessarily be closely tied up with the mother. For this reason, the mother was tested too. It appeared that some of the child's difficulties were reactive, aside from those due to the schizophrenic process.

Dr. Friend: It is essential that we see the intrapsychic aspects of the mother's role in our evaluation of the child and the effects of the mother's changes on the child.

Miss Grossman: Are the growth and development seen here over a two-year period aspects of a normal latency development in a schizophrenic child, or is this unusual?

Dr. Friend: I wish we could clarify just this question; in our present state of knowledge this is impossible. While we may say that in the schizophrenic every aspect of the personality is involved, we know that this is really inconceivable and that there are always conflict-free islands. Our problem is to ascertain which areas these are and to evaluate the possibilities of growth in these areas of the ego—or diminution in the expression of id drives. The question of the reversibility of the displacement in which the dog concept is better integrated than the human one is basic in this case. In such cases as this, where the animal is not used as a phobic object but is used in reality, with the exclusion of human object representation, the problem is particularly difficult.

Miss Levinger: In this connection, I should point out the necessity of differentiating the child whose totem object is better than the human representation from one in which the two are equal. Can Miss Werner tell us whether this child shows a sort of psychic "double-entry bookkeeping" in which the psychotic ideation is more intense along with a greater social awareness?

Miss Werner: Yes, this is so. The material presented by this child shows a quality of plausibility rather than one of repression of the psychotic trends. There is less disorganization than is usual in such cases, with some structuring of both the psychotic process and the process of perception of the outside world. Actually, most of the pathological signs seen here may be found in other children. It is their accumulation here that is significant. It is possible that the structuring we see here might be part of a normal maturation process. In any event, it is important that the child is capable of developing in this manner.

Dr. Flescher: I feel that we are here discussing the question of the reliability of psychological tests for the diagnosis of schizophrenia. I agree with the statement of Dr. Leo Stone in his paper on "The Widening Scope of Psychoanalysis"* that psychological tests can offer data which are not initially available clinically but which cannot be used for definite diagnosis or prognosis without the check of clinical data. It was Dr. van Ophuijsen who many years ago affirmed that in case of disagree-

---

* *J. Am. Psa. Assn.,* Vol. II, 1954.

ment between the clinical and psychological diagnosis, the first should determine our treatment plan.

In any case, the discussion of a psychotic process prior to the completion of the clinical presentation of the case may be misleading. We may learn that any "process" in the sense in which this concept is applied to schizophrenia does not exist in this case.

Dr. Blos: I have read many tests like this one in cases I have followed in treatment. In some, treatability was nil, while in others it emerged as something unpredictable from the psychological data. Treatability must be assessed in terms of quantitative differences. For example, contamination may occur in children with less fusion of perception and primary process than in others. Such quantitative differences are difficult to determine from tests. These may point up signs but do not make quantitative differentiations. Where there is extensive primitivity in all areas, along with the *idée fixe* of the dog, it would suggest a generally primitive way of functioning. Here, however, there is a discrepancy. The *idée fixe* is there but the drawings aren't bad. Thus the outstanding construction here—the dog—seems to be a sign of restitution in terms of a totemistic defense. This is cause for optimism.

Dr. Friend: This raises the question of what is involved in the restitutive process. In the adult it will be more developed usually, with delusion formations or paranoid development. The process of restitution in children has not been well studied. There are some who say that childhood schizophrenia differs from adult schizophrenia in that one does not see the full development of restitution. The problem is, how much of the child's energies are being used in primary processes and how much in secondary processes. The psychological report, although it is interesting, has not changed or added significantly to the data available clinically. The problems of both the psychologist and clinical observer are essentially the same.

Miss Levinger: It is important to note, however, the distinction between real intactness and the quasi-intactness shown by this child; that is, her plausibility. She does the right things for the wrong reasons. This places the problem in a somewhat different light from the clinical observations.

Dr. Friend: This ties up with the problem of therapy. The stumbling block in therapy with such cases is the assessment as real change of a seeming improvement which is only pseudo adaptation. We must be very careful in saying we have cured a schizophrenic.

Miss Levinger: One should emphasize the vitality shown by this child, which is unlike the picture of most other schizophrenics, who are weak and meager. This vitality should be available for therapy.

Mr. Sternbach: The schizophrenic is completely unpredictable and prognosis is always difficult because of this. I wonder whether the attempt at prognostication here is not unrealistic, since we really have no criteria for determining whether a schizophrenic is treatable or not. We must still operate largely on the basis of personal feeling. One way of arriving at such criteria might be to ask people who have successfully treated schizophrenics what they felt were the reasons for their success. Unfortunately, it is unlikely that any real consensus would be arrived at.

Dr. Flescher: At this point I should like to continue the presentation of the clinical material. Despite reservations, we decided to attempt outpatient therapy with this child, with mother and child seen by the same therapist. In our intention to clarify both diagnosis and prognosis, data will be offered from different levels within the personality of the child as well as in the interpersonal parent-child relationship. Miss Galdston is going to read in chronological sequence fragments from her therapeutic interviews with mother and child which have been selected by me because of their significance for the above-stated purpose. I shall preface each of these fragments by more or less epigrammatic comments of interpretive nature [printed in italics].

CASE PRESENTATION

Reality contact in play.—From time to time B. would stop in the middle of this play and would say something in her normal voice, trying to show me that she was still here.

Dog as a helper.—The mother fell into the toilet bowl, and yelled at the baby, "I'm going to kill you!" The baby yelled "Help!" and finally the dog saved the baby, carrying it off on its back.

Disguise of identity. Development of positive transference.—I asked her who she was and she said she was a friend of the baby. She told me that the baby was disguising herself as a puppy so the parents wouldn't know who she was. She wondered when I would leave here and if I would leave if I were getting married. I told her I wouldn't be leaving here until she was, and she said to me that she thought she would never be through coming here.

Deep regression in play.—The mother discovered that the baby was a dog. "The mother keeps on killing me." The baby began to dress up in "duty." Speaking as a baby, she said, "Oh, let me eat 'duties,' it is delicious."

Dog as superego.—The dog still likes her; the dog is the baby's friend. However, when the dog finds out that the baby is disgusting, it won't eat and play with her any more and it leaves her.

Therapeutic catharsis.—As we were leaving the room B. said that her headache was gone; she held me tightly. As soon as she reached her mother, she announced again that her headache was gone.

Traumatizing attitude of father: importance of control for father.—The father told me that she was mentally all there, but . . . had a mind of her own and . . . didn't accept authority. They got B. a dog but only kept it five or six months because it had a mind of its own and was hard to train. It jumped all over the place and was hard to toilet-train. He had quit school and gone to work early "like a damned fool" . . . his parents . . . had not been firm enough.

Mother: sees B. as crazy.—The mother says that . . . B. has retained the same rather strange pattern all along. B. had to take a bath alone one night and mother didn't want her to wash her hair. When she came upstairs she found B. washing her hair and got very upset about this. Mrs. D. was disturbed as to why she did this. She thinks her daughter is trying to escape reality.

Mother's own deprivation and impact on relationship with B.—When she and her husband are embracing . . . she has the feeling that his eyes are always on the clock. She suddenly asked if she had spoiled her daughter. She knows that trees need pruning to grow straight and that if they are not pruned, they grow wild . . . she has more pleasure with B. when she is firmer with her.

Dominating trend in mother and its history.—Mother said that B.'s father and maternal grandmother are dominating people. She thinks B. has inherited it from them. Her own mother is a stickler for detail. . . . She likes to have her husband feel that he is master of the house and that she hasn't taken over. She thinks it's all right for a woman to be ambitious but she is afraid that B. may try to override her husband.

Introjection of the aggressor.—After she had gotten the mother doll wet, B. screamed to the mother that she had gotten her clothes wet. She then had the mother doll spank the baby, saying to it, "You are the baby who eats 'duties' all the time. Now just watch yourself."

Affection as proof of acceptance.—She suddenly stopped and asked me did anyone ever wish they could kiss me? . . . She said, "You know what, I wish that I could kiss you." B. asked me if she could . . . I asked her what it would mean and she replied that if she could kiss me she could tell me in this way that she loved me and that if I let her kiss me I would be telling her that I like her.

Apparent disorganized verbalization and attempts at restitution (will be contradicted later).—She had the father flying around in the air and called him Superman. She sang a song in which words went: "When I am singing a song, you always get along, any time when I talk nice to your friends and relatives."

Quick return to reality and acceptance of limitation after intense regressive play.—However, the next scene was of the father hitting the mother and it finally ended up with the father and mother dancing up and down together. It started out as dancing but ended with the mother knocking the father out. When I told her that our time was up she carefully placed the little clay dog in my drawer again; she put the doll furniture back into the house so that nobody would know what she was doing. She said good-by to me cheerfully.

Mother's hostility to the child.—Mrs. D. said that all she knew was that she had a headache after the psychological tests. She felt that this was ironical since I had cured B.'s headaches. She went on to tell me that B. had brought home a bad report from school. Mrs. D. was quite punitive to B., telling her that she could have no more playtime until she started working on her schoolwork. In reaction, B. had a terrific temper tantrum and was spanked several times by her mother. She was also afraid of the vacuum cleaner and Mrs. D. had to drag her to it and make her touch it to show her that it wouldn't hurt her.

Mother's projection in educational attitude.—When I asked her what would happen if she didn't put pressure on the children, she said that they would go wild and she felt this was the fear that any mother would have.

Progress—mother's reaction.—Mother said that B. has been quite grown up this week, helping . . . getting herself ready for school. She was very pleased; she feels that B. is an extremist about everything and that when she improves she is extremely grown up and when she regresses she is extremely childish. Perhaps the improvement has to do with Christmas.

Child's increasing controls.—She felt that B. was more subdued and ladylike in her behavior. Here she explodes the moment she gets off the elevator, but . . . other places she seems to understand that her mother doesn't want her to behave this way. She had told B. to save her expressions and her feelings for the interview.

Oedipal guilt in mother.—She made a lot of mistakes in the beginning of her marriage . . . she felt younger after she was married than before. She suddenly became fourteen again, but when she was fourteen she had to pretend she was eighteen so that she could work and not get her employer into trouble. When she married it was as if she had married her father.

Increasing attachment to therapist and ability to share therapist with other children.—B. gave Checker (a dog) to the therapist; the therapist cuddled it. She said she was sad when she didn't come here—wished she could be here all the time. She knew the therapist loved her and didn't have to ask. She knew the therapist had to see other children. She wanted to take all the rubber bands, but didn't take them all because there wouldn't be enough for the other children.

DISCUSSION

Dr. Friend: Let's stop here and resume the discussion.

Miss Klein: First, I'd like to call attention to the importance of the therapist's attitude. She was not frightened by the material and did not transmit anxiety to the child.

Dr. Friend: You observed that the child's expression of the helpfulness of therapy and of how she misses the therapist evoked love in return. The fact that the therapist accepts her thinking helps the child to develop better reality testing.

Miss Adelberg: The child knows what the therapist is doing in helping her toward better reality orientation and sees the therapist doing what the mother should do.

Mrs. Kolodney: I wonder if the therapeutic process here is different from that with a child with a less severe psychological report and less obvious psychopathology.

Miss Galdston: I never thought of this child comparatively, and in working with her I focused on her specific functioning, first by observing her and then by identifying myself with the feeling of the dog in her fantasies, so as to get into the primary process. Then I sought to draw the child back into reality.

Dr. Friend: Then there are no essential differences in the approach here from that used in dealing with any child. The basic procedures of setting up a relationship, acceptance and noninterruption of material apply here as well as with others.

Dr. Blos: The incorporation of the therapist as a part of her life is unusual for a child of this age. She borrows ego identity from the therapist. This is never seen in neurotic children.

Dr. Friend: Indeed it is seen only in schizophrenic children and in a lot of them. This kind of schizophrenic child incorporates good objects and thus feels good. The feeling good represents more than just the result of catharsis; it reveals the child's primitive capacity for introjection as part of her identification mechanisms—just as she does with the dog, really.

Dr. Flescher: The ego core is always formed by positive experiences with the mother. This child had none of these with her tangibly punitive mother. Thus the new corrective experience in therapy strengthens the ego; this, however, is not specific for schizophrenics. The age doesn't matter here; what counts is that the child's regression has been accepted without anxiety or punishment and then she is led back to reality.

Dr. Friend: What is under discussion here is the splitting of objects as opposed to diffuseness of object relations. We know that with this child Miss Galdston is seen consistently as the "good" object; another type of child can't sustain one type of object. In such a case we know that things would be more difficult. This child is easier to handle therapeutically than one with a diffuse, constantly changing picture.

Mrs. Feldman: Such a diffuse picture would certainly elicit anger in the therapist and would be harder to tolerate. In this case the child is always loved by the therapist.

Mr. Sternbach: An important factor here is the low degree of aggression directed at the therapist. In such a case there is no need for the latter to project his own aggression; at least not so far. This may be decisive for the prognosis.

Miss Klein: It is important to note that this child always keeps contact with the bounds of reality. There is a great deal of fantasy play, but she always knows it is playing and always gets back to reality. It is this, as opposed to other children in whom there is a spill-over of primary-process activity into the relationship with the therapist, that led us to the conclusion that placement was not necessary in order to set limits for this child.

Dr. Bernabeu: I think we must consider Dr. John Rosen's contention that transference is not something created by the therapist, but represents the need for love on the part of the patient which flows into the outlet provided by the therapeutic situation. It doesn't mean that the child is schizophrenic if she takes advantage of the possibility of fulfillment of this need.

Dr. Friend: Anna Freud reports that children have the capacity for transference in the oral and anal phases of development. Here we see manifestations of oral need in a later period of development to a degree which is remarkable for a nine-year-old. Dr. Blos has pointed out the usual extent of this here.

Mrs. Lehnert: The child develops her inner conflicts in the therapeutic situation in a logical sequence. This is unusual for a schizophrenic child. The material, with the sharp differentiations between id, ego and superego, doesn't sound like that of a schizophrenic child.

Dr. Friend: It may be that the easy flow here is related to the fact that Miss Galdston has not yet begun to frustrate this child. In relation to Mrs. Lehnert's point one might ask whether, with just this material before us, we would think of a neurosis or of possible schizophrenia. Children develop in their use of symbolic material, based on maturation and other factors. The bizarre material here may not be schizophrenic, but it is certainly like the production of a much younger child. The content is not the criterion—it is the form and dynamics that count. The intensity of this child's involvement with her conflict indicates the depth of her regression.

Miss Adelberg: All of this material doesn't represent the

child's real conflicts. It looks like a movie which is just told about, not felt.

Miss Klein: The child walks into the office and barks like a dog and everyone turns around to look. It is very realistic.

Dr. Friend: This is primary-process identification of unusual quality.

Dr. Flescher: I disagree strongly. The concern that the child showed about other children is of decisive importance. This child is able, through her awareness of the good feelings of the therapist, to respond in return with her own positive feelings and then to share them with other children. As it often happens one might unknowingly duplicate the mother's attitude if one sees this child as crazy; there is an inclination to project one's own irrational unconscious onto a child with puzzling clinical features, to the detriment of our therapeutic effort.

Dr. Friend: This child is in a position where she is getting a positive response from the therapist, while in a different dynamic position with her mother. The mother is, indeed, almost lost. The ease with which this child can get into this position without a feeling of loss is remarkable. The changes in the child have been rapid and dramatic, with the mother persisting with her same inner attitudes throughout, seeing the changes, tempering her behavior and feeling relief. The mother shows great infantile possessiveness as well as a cruel sadistic rearing, as indicated by her remarks about "pruning the tree." Every child with such a mother doesn't, however, show such a picture.

Dr. Flescher: The progress of treatment was for some time safeguarded by the fact that the mother has persisted in her punitiveness. Otherwise, B.'s transference would have been overloaded with guilt. The child has been able to separate the good therapist from the bad mother. The use of this defense was indispensable for that period.

Dr. Friend: What about the effects on the child of giving up the mother or making her an exclusively bad object? This represents a remarkable splitting of the object.

Dr. Bernabeu: For instance, was there any evidence in the child of depression setting in as a result of the object loss?

Miss Klein: No, the child began to play the therapist off against the mother, showing overt affection for the therapist in front of the mother. The mother became angry when the child did this, so angry with the therapist that she threatened to withdraw.

Dr. Friend: Thus far the accent has been on the positive aspects of the case, with the exception of my own emphasis on the negatives. I propose that at the next interdisciplinary meeting those presenting try to summarize the trends in the material. The emphasis will be on the use of the therapeutic material in helping us to evaluate our diagnosis and increase our dynamic understanding of this fascinating case.

III

Dr. Friend: This is the third and last meeting we will devote to this case. More and more elements have been gathered in therapy which we would like to have known at the beginning. The emphasis today will be on the use of the therapeutic material in helping us to evaluate our initial diagnosis. Dr. Flescher and Miss Galdston will continue with the case presentation.

Case Presentation

Why B. sings at the top of her lungs even in front of strangers.—Mother told me that three months after marriage she had a spontaneous collapse of her lungs and had to be in bed. She used to lie in bed and sing great operas in her mind. She commented that one of the reasons that her husband never knew what she felt was because instead of having the battles with him, she would have them within herself. I asked her about this singing of great operas and she told me that she was shy as a little girl and would have liked very much to sing. As a matter of fact, she thinks it is funny that B. sings in front of people and can act and do all the things she would have liked to do. The neighbors think that B. sings because of happiness but Mrs. D. thinks it is a cover-up for fear. She herself used to sing a lot when she was a child and was lonely.

Mother as a cruel teacher.—Mrs. D. began today by telling me of B. learning to skate, and commenting on the way the child had learned to walk. She was all right until somebody came near her or talked to her and then she got hysterical. Mrs. D. slapped her daughter to break the hysteria and "of course the slap resulted in a bloody nose." When I asked Mrs. D. to describe the hysteria to me, she said that the child raised her voice and it seemed a combination of anger and fear.

Growing of social feelings.—B. said we should go and say hello to the little girl who was seeing me next. I said that she could say hello if she wanted to and she walked up to Mary, saying hello in a very sweet voice and Mary returned her greeting. As we walked back to my office B. said that the little girl was quite pretty. When we got back to the room she asked me if the little girl had worries and problems too, and I nodded my head, saying "Yes." She then looked up at me and stated positively that I would be able to help the little girl, wouldn't I? A few minutes after she had left my room at the end of the interview she came back with her hat and coat on and said that the little girl who is waiting to see me wondered if I was going to see her.

Child tests worker to make sure she is unlike her mother.—I went on to say that somebody should hold a little puppy when he is first learning to walk because puppies are afraid of falling. B. told me that we shouldn't talk this way to him, that we should call him a stupid dog because he is not following her directions. She told me that I should yell at the dog and tell him how to walk. I replied that I would like to help him to walk, that I didn't think he'd learn too well through yelling, that it would be more helpful if we helped him to walk by holding onto him. At one point in the interview, B. put her hand on mine and said to me, "You know, Miss Galdston, you play these games very well with me."

B.'s capacity for intense positive feelings.—B. asked me what the time was. I told her and then she asked me how many minutes she had left. I told her this and asked her if something was wrong. She sat in silence, cuddling the puppy to her face and not answering me. After this moment of silence, B. looked at me and started to cry. She got up as she started to cry and I put my arms out to her, and asked her what was the matter. She said, as she was crying, that she didn't want to leave me, that I was the only person who loved her, that she wished I were her mother. She wished that she could stay with me forever and that she would never have to leave me.

Mother's dependency and oral needs, their denial, their handling in treatment.—In this interview, Mrs. D. brought up that B. seemed to need her dogs most at bedtime. She could understand this since bedtime is a lonely time for her as well. In the past when she herself was a child it was lonely for her and now it is too.

Her husband and two children order the same things each time they go out for dinner. She was exasperated with their lack of imagination and suddenly decided that everybody should eat leg of lamb, something they rarely do. Her husband questioned her command and said that he did not see why they all had to, but she insisted and won out.

At the end of today's interview Mrs. D. dropped her gloves. I picked them up for her, for which she thanked me. Then I realized that she had left her umbrella in the office and I brought this to her as she was leaving. She giggled childishly and said: "My goodness, what would I do without you."

Mother's growing tendency to identify with deprived child.—Mrs. D. told me that B. had been thrilled with her visit to me and that she is not surprised, because she knows the child likes me and thinks about me a lot. She thinks that it is good that B. has this attachment, as it is the only way she can get help from me.

Mrs. D. paused and said that she wanted to tell me of something which had occurred after the last visit. She and B. had a talk about something which happened years ago—a kind of "mutual confession." Once when B. was acting like a dog and was wanting to be treated like one, Mrs. D. tried everything to stop this and finally in disgust she threatened to call the dog-catcher. She pretended to call him and then made her son go down and ring the bell and pretend that it was the dogcatcher coming. She remembers that B. was putting her coat on and started down the stairs while Mrs. D. went up to the roof to watch her daughter. She remembers that B. had tears in her eyes and she herself felt as though the world were crashing about her. She watched her little girl and finally called her, saying that the man must have gone some place else. Anyway, as they talked the other night, B. asked her if she had really called the dogcatcher. Mrs. D. said no, and caught the child up in her arms, hugging her and saying that she never would have sent her away. They both cried and Mrs. D. confessed to B. that she did not understand why B. had wanted to be a dog and that she was so desperate that she had to do this to try and stop her. I asked Mrs. D. how she had felt about the talk and she replied that she felt a great weight was off her heart.

She has told the child not to worry and if she has to wet her pants, it is all right and she has also given the teacher a lecture about letting B. out of the room when she has to go, despite the rules, saying that she is endangering the child's life if she doesn't, since then B. rushes home and doesn't watch the traffic lights in her preoccupation.

About early history of the dog problem.—Mrs. D. laughed and explained that she thought of how jealous her mother's dog had been of B. when she was an infant. Her mother had gotten this dog to replace Mrs. D. when she left her mother for marriage. "The dog was her companion and child."

Grandmother and dog problem.—She spoke of being gratified that the child is sitting and writing, even though her style is repetitive and childish, because in the past she couldn't sit still and concentrate.

In telling me more about the day, Mrs. D. told me that her mother's dog, who is usually unfriendly, was very amiable that day and that the children were delighted. At one point in the afternoon the grandmother called to B. after patting the dog, and said, "Let me pet you and you can be my little dog." I wondered what made her feel so angry and Mrs. D. explained that she felt that her mother was encouraging B. to be a dog and she has a funny feeling that her mother may have something to do with B.'s bizarre behavior.

Repercussion of grandmother's attitude on child via mother.—She told me that she had been thinking of our talk about her wanting to reject B., and she realized that there were many other times when she felt this way. I asked her to tell me about these and she said that when B. was an infant she (Mrs. D.) used to walk a mile and a half to her mother's home every day. She reminded me that those were the days when her mother accused her of coming to visit her in order to see and vamp her stepfather. B. would cry at night, and Mrs. D. would be furious because she herself felt like crying.

Beginning change in this regard; mother's report.—Mrs. D. told me toward the end of the hour that she was really getting better. At Christmastime when she and her husband visited her mother, she kissed her stepfather and announced to her mother that she was going to do it whether her mother liked it or not. Her mother laughed and Mrs. D. guessed that she wasn't such a threat to her as she used to be.

Dr. Flescher: The mother brings material related to B. and to her own sexual problems. She spoke with B. about the man who exposed himself to B. in the hall years ago and B. then told her mother of sex play with her brother. Mrs. D. was horrified because it reminded her of the time when she was eight and got some information about sex from a friend. She felt it was disgusting and in later interviews referred to this as "smutty." Her husband wanted her to do these things but she has protested. She thought that perhaps the children heard some of these conversations between the parents and they might have gotten their ideas from this.

Later, the mother reports to the therapist that she has engaged in a conversation with B. in which B. talked about her desire to masturbate, about having done it in the past with hands, toys and dogs and having let Brandy, her dog, lick her private parts. After overcoming her initial shock, the mother only cautioned her to use her hands. The therapist rightly recognized on the one hand B.'s progress in terms of greater confidence in her mother, but on the other hand acknowledges that the mother might have contributed to the child's sexual acting out by letting her implement her own repressed impulses. A greater need for feminine identification is noticed in B., both in dressing and in her wish for long hair. This, however, still competes with a strong wish for male identification and a little later B. admits that she often imagines having a penis and that she makes "sissy" standing, sometimes over her hand and sometimes over a piece of paper in the toilet. In addition, there was a lot of symbolic acting out by B., who would use a water gun and shoot toward the window.

About this time, a new development, although already foreshadowed, appears in so far as Mrs. D.'s identification with the therapist is acted out through her attempts to supplant the therapist in her child's life. She resents it that the therapist discusses sexual problems with the child and accuses her of having deprived her of the most "precious thing" which a parent has: that is, the complete confidence of the child. She admits having reproached B. for having asked Miss Galdston about sex and not herself, whereupon B. replied: "But you would have told me that God planted the seed." However, after she talked with B. in a more direct way, B. asked her mother if she could do it right away with her father or brother. Mrs. D. revealed at this point her own sexual fantasies; how she knew from her mother about her father's violence—when her mother refused him intercourse he threw an iron at her; how she thought that a child is completed by a sequence of intercourses and admitted that the male part of the intercourse was "the most disgusting" to her. She was always self-conscious about small discharges from her vagina, feared that they might show at the bottom of her dress, and ended up by fearing to blow her nose in the presence of people. This showed up in her quest for neatness which she even now imposes on the child as, for example, when she bought the child a paint set and then became upset because the child went over the line.

B. gives us a clue to why she internalized the dog by saying that if God would give her a real dog she would stop pretending to be one or have an imaginary one. *The role of companions as substitutes for real object relationships* is most dramatically revealed when the imaginary companion, Joan, turned out to be a substitute for a real Joan. To quote from Miss Galdston's notes, "I asked B. if she had even known a real girl by the name of Joan. She said she had. She used to be in her school and her class. I asked what she was like and B. told me that she had been the captain of the guards, was popular, and very pretty with long black hair. I asked if Joan had liked B. At this point B. stopped playing, came and sat down. With tears in her eyes she told me that Joan had not liked her, had made faces at her and had told her to go away. B. did not know why Joan did not want to be her friend, but she tagged after her and tried to be her friend. Then Joan moved away from school. I guessed that B. had wanted her as a friend so much that she had made her into an imaginary friend. B. nodded that this was true and that often she had lots of friends in her imagination. Sometimes she even became a girl at school whom she thought of as particularly nice. I thought B. must be pretty dissatisfied with herself if she had to pretend to be someone else." Evidently Joan offered to B. the opportunity to develop an ego ideal. The need for it was so great that when B. was rejected she re-created a fictitious Joan.

The mother's share in fostering the child's rich fantasy life is revealed in an interview with her, during which she says that she was lonely in her own childhood and had imaginary friends. She had a whole pale world of people in which she was a giant like Gulliver, had a lot of little people around her and used to boss them, making them do what she wanted and making them amuse her.

At what stage in treatment are we now? At this point a crisis has arisen since the family must leave the city. Since we achieved considerable progress in this case we decided to explore a little to see whether they could not handle their economic situation without moving, because the child might regress if withdrawn from therapy now. Actually they are still very vague about what they want to do and it is important to verify whether or not they are about to act out their problems by going away.

The mother apparently reacted negatively to any suggestion that the therapist see the father.

What would be the next step in treatment if it could be continued? *It seems that the outstanding aspect was the mother's use of her child to act out her own irrational impulses.* This fact is incompatible with further progress in treatment, unless the case is divided. The positive transference of mother with the therapist would make the plan to let mother and child be treated by separate therapists feasible.

DISCUSSION

Dr. Friend: If we go back to the *original complaint and symptoms,* may we ask what attitude the child now shows toward the parents? Originally the complaint of the mother was that she showed no affection to the parents.

Miss Galdston: Now there is greater evidence of affection, particularly toward the mother which the latter has reported and I have seen myself.

Dr. Friend: And the fearfulness of accidents, injuries, stairs, dark?

Miss Galdston: There is more fearfulness in terms of learning new sports, like skating and bike-riding. As far as stairs and being in the dark are concerned, none.

Dr. Friend: What has happened with her preoccupation with dogs?

Miss Galdston: It is there to some extent but not to the extent it was originally. It appears from the mother's description that at times, when she is lonely or upset about an argument or has been spanked, the dog and imaginary playmate appear, but, for instance, during week ends in the country there was no evidence of this at all. She doesn't bark as much in the interview, and not at all in school, but occasionally when walking with the mother.

Dr. Friend: And her social relationships? She was aggressive; she had to be the leader or she would withdraw completely.

Miss Galdston: I cannot comment because I have heard so little about her group activity. Recently the mother reported that she was out playing with some children and B. pushed a girl and made her fall. She felt guilty, picked her up, took her home and washed her.

Miss Grossman: Is it necessary to divide the case? Would the child be separated from Miss Galdston or would the mother?

Dr. Flescher: This child has been so deeply traumatized that I would not expose the child to separation. Mrs. D. says she has been accused by *her* mother of taking away the stepfather and her evidence of kissing the stepfather would encourage me to prepare this mother for a male therapist, and permit her to have a relationship with a male. There would be some repercussions, but in this case we would have to protect the relationship of the child with the therapist.

Dr. Friend: When Dr. Flescher is talking about the reactive factors, he is speaking about dynamics. We see the interplay between the severe sexual traumas and marked erotic stimulation that this child has undergone consistently throughout her latency period, so that the child has in a sense been reacting to a number of different aspects of the mother's own unresolved childhood conflicts. We can scarcely separate one from the other. Is the child more fragile than the mother, or the mother more fragile than the child? We have no measurements. Who regresses more?

Do we still maintain a diagnosis of schizophrenia, or have we changed some of the fundamental conceptions that we had in the first meeting? Is it a pseudo schizophrenia because we can see the reactions to the mother's personality so clearly?

Dr. Esman: I don't know why we should change our diagnostic formulation. Because we can understand the genesis of the problem in terms of the interaction between parents and child, must we assume that this is not a schizophrenic process? There is unquestionably overwhelming environmental trauma. In this case we have the reactive situations elucidated. Nonetheless, the child's problems are now intrapsychic, and I think the pathology remains schizophrenia; the pattern of functioning is still on a schizophrenic level.

Dr. Flescher: What is schizophrenic in this child?

Dr. Esman: The extent of regressive behavior; the extreme fluidity of her identification process; the bizarreness of her behavior. The fact that we understand it doesn't make it less bizarre.

Dr. Flescher: What strikes you as bizarre about this child?

Dr. Esman: Her barking; coming into the office barking.

Dr. Flescher: This is not specific to schizophrenia. Every child is entitled to reactions to particularly intense or long-lasting traumatizing environmental pressures. This child has taken over certain roles. The mother has always wanted to be an actress. Her own mother always spoke about her daughter becoming a "child star." She was shy and subdued in the presence of others and now she finds it amusing that her daughter sings at the top of her voice and approaches strangers. We saw the child enacting the role of a dog, the history of which we traced back to grandmother's reaction to the loss of her daughter with whom she had had a peculiar relationship. The latter persists to a certain degree, as we see from certain repercussions which the grandmother's attitude has on Mrs. D.

Dr. Friend: What then, is your diagnostic impression?

Dr. Flescher: The diagnostic alternatives presently at the disposal of the psychiatrist are few and limited. They do not cover the variety and degree of ego regression and still less the intensity of past and current traumata impinging on the individual and the adaptive patterns he develops under their impact.

Dr. Blos: You have given us clear illustrations of certain insights into the child's behavior. There is no doubt that a change in this child has taken place, but I would agree with Dr. Esman that if a child that age shows a kind of behavior like barking, this is bizarre. We have such fantasies with young children in identification with a dog, and a child under six will play this out, but this finally becomes a fantasy and is not really experienced any more as an ego state different from that of being a little girl. What we see here is a fragmented ego.

Dr. Flescher: Whenever the child played the role of dog, she always used a different voice. She always made it clear to the therapist that this is play. She would ask, "Can I now do something else?" She was fully aware of playing the role of a dog.

Dr. Blos: Yes, she is aware of it, but she cannot renounce it. The child knows this is play but it forces itself on her and is not simply compulsive, but is a part of herself which simply presses for a state of release.

Dr. Friend: There is a disagreement upon the evaluation of the phenomenon. This is fundamental. Dr. Flescher feels that this is a sign of acting out. Dr. Blos feels this is an emergence of some id content bursting through the ego despite the ego defenses. Most of the insight has come from the contact with the mother who elucidated all the circumstances. The basic changes therapeutically have come through transference rather than through the child's gaining insight. She is having a corrective experience with a different person. This is the kind of child who *appersonates,* who assumes and introjects some of the ego functions of the person with whom she is in contact. Yet I am not sure how much we have been able to help the child to emerge and unfold. We have frequent cases of transference improvement.

Mr. Sternbach: This barking and being a dog comes from the fact that this child has no ego structure of her own and identifies herself with the mother who sees her as a dog. This is symbiosis. This action at the age of nine is ominous.

Dr. Friend: Here is the same point that Dr. Blos has made, but Mr. Sternbach has introduced the fact that this child will seek to become a dog to please the mother.

Dr. Flescher: The child has said at a certain point that if God would give her a dog, she would stop being a dog, she would not imagine herself being a dog. The wish to be a dog certainly draws additional investment from the child's own conflicts. We saw that she wished she had a penis. The latter wish is certainly not unrelated to her wish to have a child from her father (God). At one point, B. discovered that God spelled backwards was dog. In conclusion, through the interest in drawing dogs and playing the role of a dog, many of the child's frustrations of pregenital and genital nature were acted out. The question of transference improvement versus insight can be answered with fair plausibility. The child says, "You know I have an imaginary companion, Joan," and remembers how she created her. The memory of rejection preceding the creation of an imaginary companion was the result of growing insight.

Dr. Friend: But the child is not in it, she presents it historically, but she is not reliving this.

Dr. Flescher: She is not reliving it? B. after a long period of reticence cried and accused her mother of not loving her, while expressing most dramatically to the therapist appreciation for being accepted. Only following this, B. talks about this girl rejecting her and "because she rejected me I have imagined a companion."

Mrs. Lehnert: Many years ago we had a child who identified with animals. There was no one in the outside world who wanted to make her an animal. She didn't bark or act like an animal but her ego identification was with one. The animal world was humanized.

Miss Levinger: Some of us are using schizophrenia as a 100 per cent concept. Dr. Esman thinks of this child as schizophrenic, but with strong restitutional qualities. That doesn't make her not a schizophrenic, but a different kind of schizophrenic.

Dr. Friend: All sorts of symptoms, from hallucinations to phobias, may be used in the restitutive effort to prevent utter desolation. If we go far enough, we can misuse the classification of schizophrenia for any known psychiatric disorder. Even if we agree on some of the dynamics, we still have different viewpoints as to diagnosis. A number of us have said that because of the level of introjection and regression, the same reactive factors that Dr. Flescher has pointed to imply a level of unresolved conflict. No one at the outset felt that this was going to be an easy treatment problem, whatever the diagnosis. The events, even with the increasing clarity, have not done away with this impression. While we can appreciate the dynamics, the interaction of reactive and intrapsychic factors is most complex. This child has continuously been traumatized and obtains tremendous gratification from some of her deviant behavior.

Dr. Esman: One of the things that came out in the psychological testing was the *acute observation of this child* of what is acceptable behavior in certain circumstances. This is characteristic in certain schizophrenic children—an awareness of what is socially acceptable behavior. She doesn't bark in school because she cannot get away with it. With her mother she can get away with it. In these situations she permits herself to regress but in other situations she doesn't.

Miss Klein: One of the criteria we used for taking this child on for treatment despite the fact that originally it was suggested that she be placed in a residential treatment center, was that she showed a cerain kind of intactness, that she seemed always aware that this was play. This was regarded as ego strength. There were many reactive elements in this case which we were aware of, but we felt that this could be treated in our setting. In other cases the id impulses come through more dangerously, but not in this case.

Dr. Friend: One of the things that this child has not been able to face is the extent of her aggressive drives. It is true, however, that her aggressions have been handled largely by displacement, and this kind of schizophrenic case is easier to treat than others.

Miss Adelberg: I am concerned that the child has to live with the mother and be enmeshed by the mother's fantasies. It seems we find the mother now sicker than at the beginning and learn how the mother distorts. *I do not see how we can treat the child when she lives with the mother.*

Dr. Flescher: It is a fact that the mother has become, through treatment, more accepting of the child. She brings up traumatic experiences to which she has exposed the child, and this shows that she is able to change. She subsequently, however, comes into conflict on a transference level because she would like, in competition with the therapist, to retain the confidence of the child especially around sex, repeating what the grandmother had exposed her to, like double dating, etc. *Who is the most disturbed person in this case? I think the grandmother,* because she accused her daughter of coming to visit her only for the purpose of taking her husband away.

Dr. Friend: What have we learned that we can apply? We can, in selecting cases for treatment, have the same consistent therapeutic confidence and optimism which is necessary for investigation and research. What have we determined that would be helpful to us diagnostically in the establishment of criteria for selection of cases for social work therapy?

Dr. Bernabeu: In choosing a case and in making a diagnosis I sometimes feel we are trapped by the bizarreness, and equate this with a psychotic break with reality. Very often what we consider bizarre makes us think of schizophrenia, and we feel that what happens in the second year of treatment is what we should have known at the beginning. This whole testing of reality by the child is an essential point. I do not feel from the information that this barking was such a bizarre thing because she does not bark in school. There is a danger in accepting bizarre behavioral description. One tends to handle behavior, rather than risk being overwhelmed by diffuse aggression.

Mrs. Feldman: I was very much interested in the whole discussion of the case and in the questions of the difference of diagnoses, but I have to think of it from the standpoint of a social worker, whose function is service. We do not have in this case objective information of what happened to this child. Has she really improved in her behavior? Since we do not know what "schizophrenia" is, optimism is extremely necessary. Here is a child in the latency period. If you permit her to go on without treatment, she will not be able to function in school. If, through transference, persistent gains in functioning are effected, then we have achieved a *social improvement.* If the child can live at home and get help from treatment then I would prefer this to placement.

Miss Galdston: I have found that this case has enabled us to translate something for intake. Despite our diagnosis of schizophrenia, the child was able to get something across. There was a part of an ego that was intact, that could respond to treatment and I think these children can be reached.

Mr. Sternbach: We have to summarize which cases of schizophrenia we can accept and which we cannot. We cannot accept those cases which need medical treatment. Then, what we can treat is not the illness but the adaptation. We have to look first of all to the family. If we feel the family is too rigid I think the case would be unacceptable. Then comes the picture of the child itself, which we get not so much from diagnosis but from history. To what extent can the child handle outbursts? If the child cannot control severe outbursts, then we cannot handle this. If from the history we can make this judgment, this is good; but in most cases we would have to see the child in more situations. Then the problem is how long will it take to establish contact with the child? These would be the criteria for me if I had an intake to make.

Dr. Friend: I am not so satisfied with the mixture of dynamics and behavior. I'd like to paraphrase this and see if you basically agree. I think that we have considered this from the intake worker's stance and that we need in these situations to get a genetic story and to think of the dynamics involved. What do the story and behavior describe? Is the family's pathogenic behavior stark or subtle? We would also like to be able to assess some areas where the child can function successfully. If the child is diffuse in all areas, this would be a tremendous problem. What is so striking in this case is some kind of object relation or some kind of an attempt at object relationship in the form of appersonation. The way in which the aggression manifests itself is also of some importance for us to consider. Another factor is the onset of the illness. The process doesn't have to begin at birth, but can start at a definite age. The problems of treatment of *autistic* development are inordinate at the present time. We would not consider this kind of child.

I think that what we have learned is the following: if we are given a child with such severe pathology as B., there would be a need for dividing the case early and for an opportunity for the therapist of the child to maintain contact with the parent. There must be some contact between the mother of such a child and the therapist of the child, regardless of the therapy of the mother, to handle what we know is involved in this reactive relationship. We would also like cases where there is a certain amount of intelligence and perceptivity, and I think we should prefer the child who is not too overwhelmed by id content. This is a marked change for us because we have in the past basically agreed not to accept schizophrenic children. It remains to be seen whether there is a basic difference between this child and other children with preoedipal disorders. Actually what we have observed here has been a necessity for the therapist dynamically to get into a position of some kind of identification with the child. The child is able to allow this kind of ingress more than a neurotic child or one with a primary behavior disorder.

INDEX

Abortion, 134
Accident-proneness, 29
Acting out, 17, 67, 74, 84, 88, 117, 153, 199, 201
Adelberg, H., 172, 190, 192, 207
Adolescent(s), 177
  atypical, 108-123
  disturbed, 91
  see also Group therapy
Affect Hunger, 86
Agency, 21, 25-26, 36, 42, 109
Aggression, 29, 41, 48, 82-83, 87, 105, 110, 112, 144, 145, 147, 152, 158, 167, 168, 173, 174, 191, 207, 209
  oral, 62
Alexander, F., 49, 50, 76
Allergies, 134, 137
Alpert, A., vii, 124-138
Alt, H., ix, xiii, 76
Ambivalence, 48, 51, 70, 73, 158
American Journal of Orthopsychiatry, ix
Anal phase, 192
Anxiety, 13, 24, 26, 27-28, 34, 41, 48, 61, 63, 66, 67, 69-70, 74, 80, 82, 83, 85, 87, 98, 111, 127, 133, 135-136, 137-138, 146, 153, 158, 179, 191
  castration, 68
  constellation, 82
  hysteria, 39, 40, 57, 65
Attention, 14, 15
Autism, 178, 209; see also Child, autistic
Autoerotic activity, 177, 180

Bank, B., vii, 124-138
Behavior, 98, 180, 206, 208-209

bizarre, 110, 146-147, 152, 165, 176, 192, 198, 203, 207-208
compulsive, 111; see also Compulsiveness
control of, 160; see also Control
delinquent, 110
destructive, 153-154; see also Aggression
disorders, see sub individual disorders
disorganized, 14, 110, 111, 154, 168
distortions of, 99
disturbed, 13, 102
impulsive, 110; see also Impulsiveness
infantile, 111, 112, 113
parental, see Parents; Parental perplexity
regressive, 110, 111, 112, 203; see also Regression
ritualistic, 111
withdrawn, see Withdrawal
Behrens, M., vii, 157-169
Bender, L., 157, 169
Bergman, P., 141, 156
Bernabeu, E., 172, 179, 181, 192, 194, 207-208
Bettelheim, B., 106
Bisexuality, 70
Bleuler, E., xi
Bloom, M., 106
Blos, P., 172, 185, 191, 204
Borderline disturbances, 39, 44, 47, 61, 65, 66, 109, 114, 183
Bottle-feeding, 10, 174
Brain damage, 6, 12, 41
Breast-feeding, 174
Bruch, H., 164, 169
Brunswick, R. M., 71, 76